Geography in a Changing World

Book Two
Understanding Developing Places

Laurence Kimpton

Hodder and Stoughton
London Sydney Auckland Toronto

Contents

Note to Teachers

The emphasis of this book is on the development and understanding of concepts which help to explain the geography of the developing world. At the same time, skills of increasing complexity are introduced. The exercises are closely integrated with the text, photographs, maps and diagrams as it is considered that children learn effectively by actively using the material presented. The level of difficulty of the exercises varies considerably and teachers should judge the extent to which particular exercises need to be preceded by discussion.

Many of the exercises call for pupils to work on copies of the maps and diagrams, so it is desirable to have duplicated copies of such materials ready.

The author is grateful to the following for supplying help and information:

Christian Aid; Costain International Ltd; Hong Kong Government; LAMCO J.V. Operating Co; Dr. P. K. Mitchell.

The publisher thanks the following for giving permission to reproduce photographs in this book:

Aerofilms (2.2); A. Archer (1.1tr, 1.4, 1.15 cent l, 3.3, 3.7a, 3.9, 3.20, 4.1a, 4.16, 8.25a, b, c, 9.1f); Barnaby's Photo Library (4.4, 8.5, 8.9); J. A. Binns (5.7); Dr. J. F. E. Bloss (3.10, 3.11); British Steel Corporation (6.10, 6.14, 7.13); Brooke Bond Oxo Ltd. (5.3); Camera Press (2.5, 2.6, 10.6); Centre for World Development Education (1.18, 4.12, 4.13, 8.23a, b, c); Christian Aid (1.1t cent,1.1bl, 1.15 cent r, 3.19, 8.1f, 8.11, 8.30a, 9.1b, 9.1g, 9.8, 9.18); Information Directorate General of the Commission of the European Communities (3.18a, b, c, d, e, f, 8.30b, c); Commonwealth Institute (2.17c, 6.18, 7.7, 7.11b); Costain International Ltd. (10.1, 10.3, 10.13a, b, c, d, e, f, 10.14); L. Davis (1.15t cent, 3.2, 3.7b, c); Dominique Pierre Foundation (Islands of Peace) (3.13, 3.15); F.A.O. (1.1tl, 1.26, 8.1a, b, c, d, 8.13, 8.15, 8.16a, b, c, d, e, 8.17, 9.15a, b); Geoslides (Photography) (7.11a, 9.1d, h, 9.9, 9.10); Hong Kong Government (9.12, 9.13, 9.14); I.L.O. (9.27a); LAMCO J.V. Operating Co. (2.17b, 6.8, 6.9); Malaysian High Commission (6.16c, d); Malaysian Rubber Research and Development Board (2.17a, 5.12, 5.13, 5.20, 5.22); Massey Ferguson (1.1 cent l, 8.24c); Dr. P. K. Mitchell (1.3a, 1.15bl cent, 1.15br, 1.20a, 1.22, 2.3, 2.14, 3.29, 3.32b, 5.9, 7.1, 7.5, 7.8, 9.19b); National College of Agricultural Engineering (8.24a, b, d); Dr. M. Peil (9.1a, e, 9.16, 9.17, 9.19a) R.T.Z. Services Ltd. (6.16a, b); Shell (7.21); Port of Singapore Authority (7.19, 7.20, 7.26a); Singapore Tourist Board (7.24, 7.26b, c, d); Tanzanian High Commission (9.26); Varig Brazilian Airlines (2.28, 10.19); J. W. Walden (3.32a); S. Watt (8.24e); Prof. G. J. Williams (1.20b); World Bank Group (9.27b); W.H.O. (9.11).

All other photographs were supplied by the author.

Printed in Hong Kong for
Hodder and Stoughton Educational,
a division of Hodder and Stoughton Ltd,
Mill Road, Dunton Green, Sevenoaks, Kent,
by Colorcraft Ltd.

1 Patterns in the environment

What is a developing place?

The title of this book, *Developing Places*, suggests that it is about those parts of the world which are not yet fully *developed*. A *developed* country is often thought of as one which has modern farms, many industries, a well-developed transport system and relatively prosperous people. The countries of Western Europe and North America are developed countries. The term 'developing' is rather hopeful; it suggests that some progress is being made. Developing countries are also known as *underdeveloped*. They are countries with many problems such as hunger, poverty and disease. Farming methods are often primitive, providing scarcely enough for people to eat, and there may be little manufacturing industry. Many of the problems of such countries are growing more and more severe because their rate of population growth is very high. This group of countries are often referred to by yet another term—*The Third World*. The First World countries are the developed ones of North America and Western Europe together with Japan, the Republic of South Africa, Australia and

Fig. 1.1
Contrasts between countries

New Zealand. The Second World countries are the Communist states of Eastern Europe. Two-thirds of the world's population live in the developing countries or the Third World.

> *Exercise 1.1*
> Figure 1.1 shows some contrasting scenes of developed and developing places. Using information from the photographs, write an account of the differences between developed and developing countries.

The photographs in Figure 1.1 have deliberately been chosen to show contrasts between developed and developing countries. It should be remembered, however, that underdevelopment may be a problem in some areas of developed countries.

Most of the developing countries are located in tropical areas, as can be seen in Figure 1.2. Because of this, you might at first think that the developing countries have very similar conditions of climate, soils and relief (the form of the land), features which together make up the natural environment, the background for man's activities. However, conditions vary widely, as we shall see in the rest of this chapter.

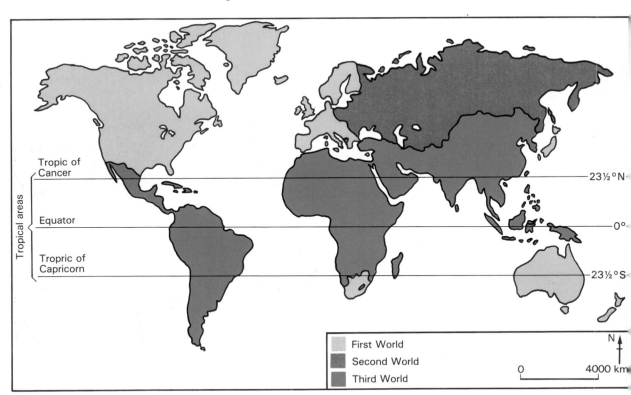

Fig. 1.2
The three worlds

Forests, deserts and mountains

Figure 1.3 shows two contrasting environments or natural backgrounds which exist in the developing countries. Quite clearly, *relationships* exist between the amount of rainfall and the type of vegeta-

Fig. 1.3
(a) Tropical rain forest—mean
annual rainfall over 1500 mm
(b) Desert—mean annual
rainfall under 250 mm

Fig. 1.4
Mount Kilimanjaro

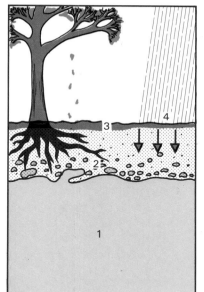

1 Solid rock, the soil's 'parent material'
2 Sub-soil with large particles of weathered rock
3 Humus layer of the soil, formed from decayed vegetation
4 Heavy rainfall washes humus and minerals to lower layers of the soil where it is of little use to plants.

Fig. 1.5
The soil

tion. The desert with its scattered, drought-resistant plants is a direct result of lack of rainfall. On the other hand, the tropical rain forest reflects the heavy rainfall (and high temperatures) occurring there throughout the year. If we also consider the shape and form of the land (*relief*) more relationships will stand out. Figure 1.4 shows Mount Kilimanjaro in East Africa, which is almost on the Equator. It is clear that with increasing height, temperatures must become lower and this in turn will affect the nature of the vegetation.

The rocks of the earth's crust which make up the relief of the land also provide the minerals in the *soil* (Figure 1.5). The nature of the soil will also depend on the supply of dead vegetation and the amount of rainfall it receives. In turn, the soil's quality will affect the nature of the vegetation growing on it. Climate, vegetation, relief, and soils together make up the natural environment which forms the background to man's activities. The effect of the environment will be most direct on farming.

Figure 1.6 shows the features of the environment that we have just looked at. However, the relationships which we have studied have not been shown on the diagram.

Exercise 1.2
Make a copy of Figure 1.6. Read carefully, again, through the last section and add arrows to the diagram where one feature affects another. For example, climate has an effect on vegetation, so an arrow should point from climate to vegetation.

Some relationships have not been mentioned and may not be so obvious. Vegetation has some effect on climate, even if it is very local, such as trees acting as a windbreak. Climate has an effect on relief; can you think how?

Exercise 1.3
(a) Add arrows to your diagram to show these other relationships. Write by the arrow going from climate to relief the ways in which features of climate shape the surface of the earth.
(b) Figure 1.6 includes an empty box for something in the environment we have not yet mentioned—animal life. Animal life will, of course, range from the higher animals, some of which will eat the vegetation, to bacteria living in the soil. Label the blank box 'Animals' and put a suitable drawing in it. Then add arrows to and from this box to show the relationships which exist between animals and other features of the environment.

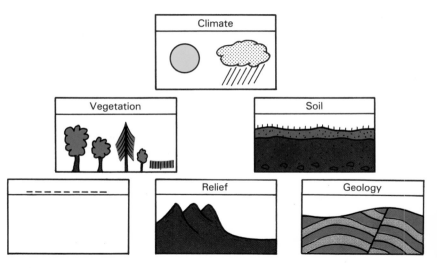

Fig. 1.6
The ecosystem

The diagram will now be quite complicated, showing many relationships. Such a set of relationships is a *system*. This system existing in nature is called the *ecosystem*. Any change in one part of the ecosystem will have effects on the other parts.

Water: the key to life on the earth's surface

The key to the working of the ecosystem is water. An environment without water would be like the surface of the moon. Water is needed for plants to grow and animals to live. Water flowing across the surface of the earth forms rivers, which wear away the hills. The part that water plays in the environment can be seen in Figure 1.7, which shows the *hydrological cycle*. Notice that the water is not necessarily in the liquid form we can see; the water rising from the earth's surface is in the form of a gas known as water vapour.

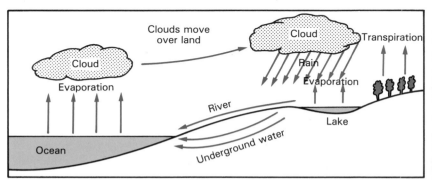

Fig. 1.7
The hydrological cycle

Let us have a closer look at the part of the hydrological cycle which involves clouds forming and rain falling. Figure 1.8 shows two ways in which clouds form and rainfall is caused, both being of great importance in tropical areas, where the developing countries are found. Notice that both ways involve air containing water vapour being forced to rise. When air rises through the atmosphere it moves into cooler and less dense layers and will therefore expand. When air expands it cools because the heat is spread out through a greater volume. Cooling causes the water vapour in the air to condense into droplets and so form clouds. This is because the cooler air is, the less water vapour it can hold, as can be seen when warm air meets a cold window pane and water droplets form on the glass.

Patterns on a continental scale

The important conclusion we can draw from the two diagrams in Figure 1.8 is that the amount of rainfall is likely to be high in areas where heating by the sun is great (provided that the air is moist) and/or where there are mountain ranges. Figure 1.9 shows two maps of South America. One shows mean (average) annual rainfall totals. The other shows mountainous areas and areas where temperatures are high throughout the year. When the maps are compared, the conclusion we drew from the rainfall diagrams appears to be supported. Areas of high rainfall tend to be similar in distribution to areas subject to great heating and, to a lesser extent, to mountainous areas.

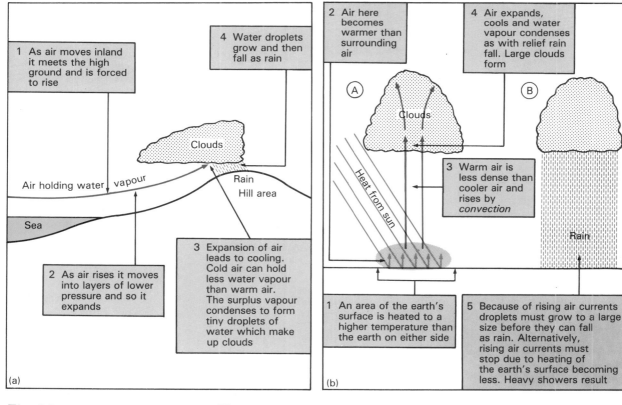

Fig. 1.8
Two types of rainfall
(a) Relief rainfall
(b) Convectional rainfall

If patterns on two maps are similar there is said to be a *correlation* between them. This visual correlation between two patterns does not always mean that a relationship exists in which one causes the other. In the case of these two maps, the diagrams of Figure 1.8 showed that there *is* a relationship as well. The patterns do not match exactly because we have not considered some of the other factors which affect the distribution of rainfall, such as the direction from which the wind most commonly blows (the *prevailing wind*).

8

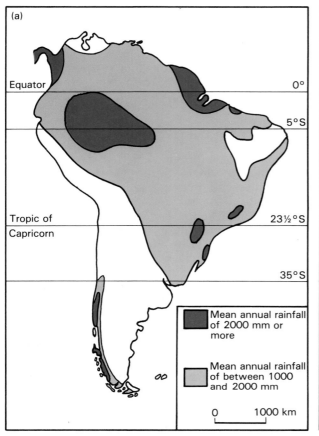
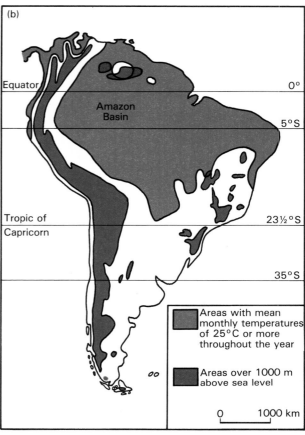

Fig. 1.9
South America
(a) Mean annual rainfall
(b) Mountain areas and areas where temperatures are high throughout the year

Exercise 1.4
(a) Look at the hydrological cycle in Figure 1.7. Explain why, if the prevailing wind is blowing from the sea to the land, rainfall may be expected to be higher than if the prevailing wind was in the opposite direction.
(b) Along the west coast of South America, the prevailing wind is south-easterly between latitudes 5°S and 35°S but is westerly south of 35°S. Look again at Figure 1.9. Explain how the directions of the prevailing winds account for the facts that:
(i) rainfall is fairly low over the central Andes;
(ii) rainfall is high over the southern Andes.
(c) On an outline map of South America copy the rainfall distribution from Figure 1.9(a). Name the Amazon Basin and label an arrow pointing to it Convectional rainfall due to intense heating of moist air. Name the Andes and indicate by arrows the directions of the prevailing winds off the west coast of South America. Give the map a key and a suitable title.

The total amount of rainfall received in a year is obviously of great importance for plant and animal life, and also for influencing the type of farming which may be carried on. The seasonal distribution of rainfall is also very important. Figure 1.10 shows the distribution of rainfall for South America, north of the Tropic of Capricorn (a) during November to April and (b) during May to October. Figure 1.11 shows the main zones of vegetation in the same area.

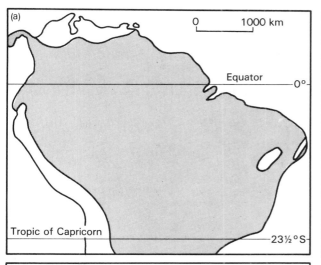

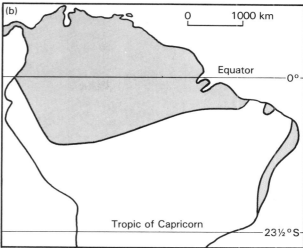

Fig. 1.10
South America north of the Tropic of Capricorn
(a)   Areas with over 750 mm of rainfall from November to April
(b)   Areas with over 750 mm of rainfall from May to October

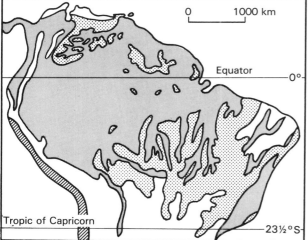

▦	Tropical rain forest (including mountain forest)
⣿	Tropical grasslands (savanna)
▨	Desert

Areas left blank include mountain areas, semi-desert and areas of temperate woodland

Fig. 1.11
South America north of the Tropic of Capricorn: major types of vegetation.

Rainfall distribution and amounts	Vegetation
Under 750 mm from November to April AND from May to October —DRY ALL YEAR	
Over 750 mm from November to April only— SEASONAL RAINFALL	
Over 750 mm from May to October only— SEASONAL RAINFALL	
Over 750 mm from November to April AND from May to October— RAINFALL ALL YEAR	

Fig. 1.12
Rainfall patterns and vegetation in tropical areas

Exercise 1.5
(a)   As a base map you will need a copy of the vegetation map in Figure 1.11. On a piece of tracing paper trace:
(i)   the coastline,
(ii)   the area with over 750 mm of rainfall from November to April (from Figure 1.10(a)),
(iii)   in another colour, the area with over 750 mm of rainfall from May to October (from Figure 1.10(b)).
Shade in the area receiving over 750 mm of rainfall in both seasons. Fix the tracing paper over your vegetation map.
(b)   The vegetation and rainfall maps, while not matching exactly, show a large degree of correlation. Complete Figure 1.12 so as to summarise the main relationships between vegetation and rainfall distribution.

The Andes Mountains are the main area where vegetation and rainfall distribution do not show a clear correlation. We shall have a closer look in a later chapter at the patterns which exist in tropical highlands. The amount of rainfall and decreasing temperature with height are important factors in such areas.

Patterns in a tropical region: climate and crops in West Africa

Fig. 1.13
Climate/vegetation zones in West Africa

West Africa is a region within the tropics which has clear zones of climate and vegetation. It is relatively densely populated and so is a good example to use in looking at the influence of the environment on man's farming activities. The main climate/vegetation zones in West

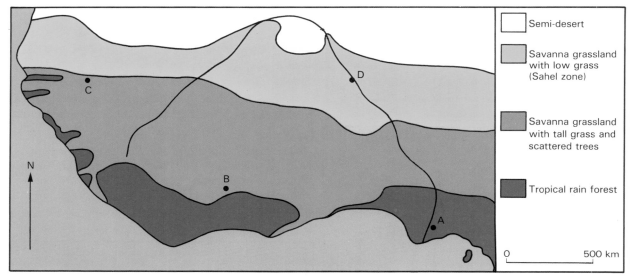

Legend:
- Semi-desert
- Savanna grassland with low grass (Sahel zone)
- Savanna grassland with tall grass and scattered trees
- Tropical rain forest

0   500 km

Location on map (Figure 1.13)	Annual rainfall	Distribution of rainfall
A (Tropical rain forest)	2100 mm	Rain occurs in every month
B (Savanna)	1250 mm	Wet season: April—October Dry season: November—March
C (Savanna)	750 mm	Wet season: May—October Dry season: November—April
D (Sahel)	300 mm	Wet season: June—September Dry season: October—May

Fig. 1.14
Rainfall totals and distribution in West Africa

Africa are shown in Figure 1.13. In Figure 1.14 climatic details are given for places A, B, C and D on the map (Figure 1.13). Figure 1.15 gives details of the rainfall needs of some important subsistence and cash crops grown in the area. (Subsistence crops are grown by a farmer for his own needs; cash crops are sold off the farm and will probably be exported.) The temperatures needed for these crops will generally be adequate in all zones. What is more important in deciding which zones they can be grown in, is their rainfall needs. This is in contrast to temperate areas such as Britain, where temperature makes one season distinct from another and is as important as rainfall as an influence on the distribution of crops.

Exercise 1.6

(a)   Make a copy of Figure 1.16. Decide which crops can be grown at locations A, B, C and D in Figure 1.13 by studying:
(i)   the climatic needs of the crops (Figure 1.15),
(ii)   the climatic details of the four locations (Figure 1.14).
Put ticks in the spaces in your table where crops can be grown. For example, cocoa can be grown at A so a tick should be placed in the space in the cocoa column against A.
(b)   Answer the following questions by looking at your completed table:
(i)   Which crops can be grown in only one climate/vegetation zone?
(ii)   Which crops can be grown most widely?
(iii) Which zone has conditions generally unsuitable for the cultivation of a wide range of crops?

Cocoa-Mean annual rainfall over 1750 mm.
Rain needed throughout year.

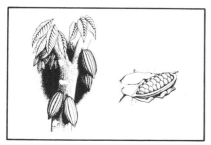

Coffee-Mean annual rainfall between 1000 and 2500 mm.
Can survive a dry season.

Groundnuts-Mean annual rainfall between 500 and 750 mm.
Dry season needed for harvesting.

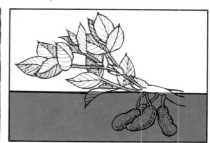

Bananas—Mean annual rainfall between 1300 and 2500 mm.
Rain needed throughout year.

Cotton-Mean annual rainfall over 500 mm.
Dry season needed.

Fig. 1.15
Some important crops grown in West Africa

Yams-Mean annual rainfall between 500 and 10000 mm.
Prefers rain throughout year but can stand a 5 month dry season.

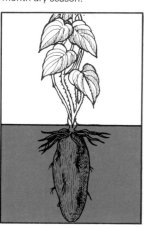

Oil palm-Mean annual rainfall between 2000 and 3000 mm.
Rain needed throughout year.

Maize-Mean annual rainfall between 250 and 5000 mm.
Rainfall distribution not important.

Millet-Mean annual rainfall between 280 and 400 mm.
Dry season needed.

Place	Climate/vegetation zone	Crops								
		Cocoa	Coffee	Oil palm	Groundnuts	Bananas	Cotton	Yams	Maize	Millet
A	Tropical rain forest									
B	Savanna									
C	Savanna									
D	Sahel									

Fig. 1.16
Where can crops be grown?

Fig. 1.17
Cash crops in West Africa

Figure 1.17 shows where a few of the cash crops are actually grown. Although climatic conditions may permit them to be grown throughout a zone, whether they are actually grown or not will depend on many things such as soils, the wishes of the farmer, encouragement

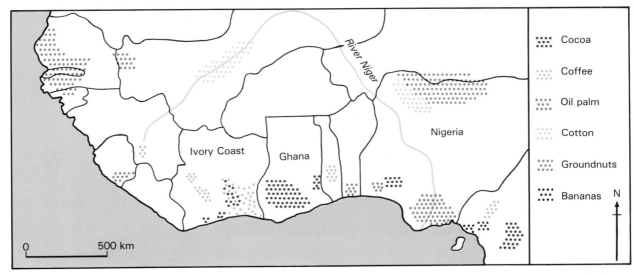

from the government or a large company, but especially on whether there is transport available to take crops to ports for export. This last factor explains why the distribution of most cash crops is more patchy than the distribution of most subsistence crops. We must also bear in mind that man may overcome climatic limits if, for example, he uses water from rivers or wells to grow crops in a dry area. This explains why cotton is widely grown in the Sahel zone.

Patterns in a small area
1. Part of a river valley in West Africa

So far, we have looked at patterns in the environment on the large scale of a continent or a major region. On a smaller scale, local differences in relief, soil and water supply affect the distribution of crops and the siting of villages. The map in Figure 1.19 is of an area of savanna grassland with a major river, important for transport, crossing it. Strips of land of varying type run roughly parallel to the river. This pattern is typical of the small country of The Gambia in West Africa.

Fig. 1.18
A field of groundnuts

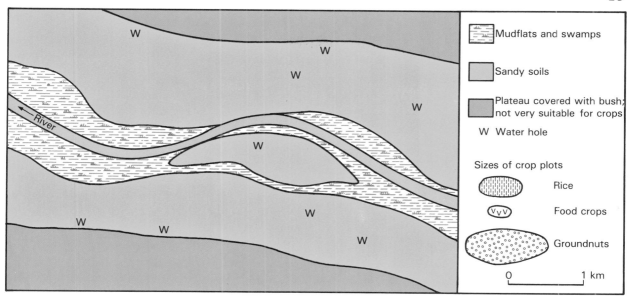

Fig. 1.19
Base map for Exercise 1.7: a river valley in West Africa

Fig. 1.20
The Gambia River
(a) Aerial view of the mouth of the Gambia River. Near the river are mangrove swamps. The road runs through farm land
(b) Boats on the Gambia River loading up with groundnuts

Exercise 1.7

Make a copy of Figure 1.19. Study the information on the map carefully. The people of The Gambia cultivate rice and vegetables for their own use, and groundnuts (peanuts) as a cash crop. Imagine that you are the chief of a tribe which cultivates these crops. The tribe needs to establish five villages, each with patches of rice, food crops and groundnuts, in the area shown on the map. Figure 1.21 gives details of the requirements of these crops. The sizes of the patches of crop adequate for one village are shown in the key to Figure 1.19. Village sites are influenced by the availability of fresh water and by the ease of access to the cultivated patches, especially to the vegetable plots.

(a) On your map, mark in the best sites for the five villages and the location of the patches of rice, food crops and groundnuts for each village. The patches must be about the same size but not necessarily the same shape as those in the key to Figure 1.19.

(b) The export of groundnuts is increasing, as is the demand for manufactured goods. The river is the main transport route. Find a suitable site on the map for a river port combined with market town and label it clearly. (Make sure that the town is not sited on swampland.)

(c) Join the villages by tracks to the market town, but avoid the ground liable to flood as far as possible.

(d) Add a key to your map to explain all the features you have marked on it.

(e) Write an account of how the physical environment of this area (relief, soils, water) has influenced the distribution of crops and the location of villages.

Rice	Must be grown on land which can be flooded by river
Food crops	Vegetables, millet and sorghum grown as subsistence crops. Frequent visits must be made to plots for daily food supplies and to cultivate and manure the land
Groundnuts	Grown as the main cash crop. Require light sandy soils

Fig. 1.21

14

Fig. 1.22
Mangrove swamp

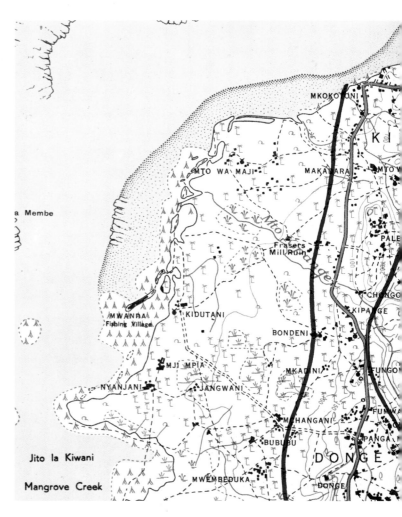

REFERENCE

Main Roads Tarmac Surface	Quarry. Cave
Secondary Roads Metalled	Lighthouse
District Roads Earth	Leading Light
Tracks	Leading Mark
Footpaths	Well. Tank
Palms. Cloves	Mosque
Mango. Orange	Mangroves
Bush and Rocks	Marsh. Rice
Sand. Flat Rock	Streams
Cliff	Contours

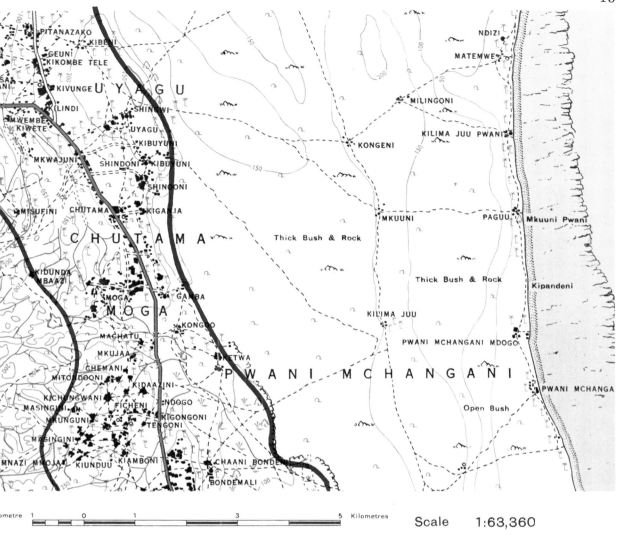

Fig. 1.23
Northern Zanzibar

2. Villages in Zanzibar

The map extract in Figure 1.23 is of an area in Zanzibar, which is part of Tanzania in East Africa (see Figure 1.24). In this area, the effect of relief and water supply on the location of villages is very striking indeed. The types of land found in this area are as follows:

1. Ridge of higher ground, deeply cut into by streams, with thin soils—very little settlement.
2. Coral platform with no surface streams and much bare rock—very little settlement. (A coral platform is made up of limestone formed from the skeletons of corals, tiny sea creatures joined to each other in great colonies.)
3. Flat coastal marshes with some mangrove swamps—little settlement because of flooding and insects.
4. Edges of ridge of higher ground, not cut into by streams but near to water supplies; thicker soil—many villages.

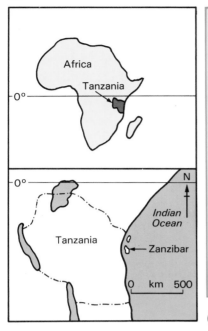

Fig. 1.24
The location of Zanzibar

Exercise 1.8
(a)   The bold lines drawn on the map extract separate areas of the four types of land. Place a piece of tracing paper over the map and trace these lines and the coastline. Now decide which of the descriptions of the four types of land listed above fit each of the divisions on your trace. Shade the types of land in as follows:

     Land type 1—brown,
     Land type 2—orange,
     Land type 3—light blue,
     Land type 4—green.

Then trace the course of the main roads in red and mark in the position of each named village with a black dot. Fix your map in your notebook and add a detailed key to explain it.
(b)   (i)   Explain carefully why most villages are found on Land type 4.
(ii)   Why are there a few villages on the coast?
(iii)   Two important crops grown in Zanzibar are rice and cloves (a spice). Describe where both of these are grown, suggesting reasons.
(iv)   Explain the course of the main roads.

Overcoming the problems of the environment

In many areas of the world man lives in a difficult environment which presents many problems for farming. He therefore has to adapt his farming methods to try to overcome these problems. The photograph in Figure 1.26 shows cultivation in Yemen, where there are problems of lack of water and steep slopes to overcome. Also, when rain does fall, it usually comes in the form of heavy downpours; the water rushes down the hillsides and washes away the soil, even on gentle slopes. Over many centuries the Yemeni farmers have built terraces on the hillsides so that they can cultivate the slopes and stop the soil being washed away. Wells have been bored in order to provide additional water for the crops. Thus, much work has been necessary so that the land can be farmed effectively. In Chapter 8 we will be having a detailed look at the ways in which farmers can overcome problems of environment.

Exercise 1.9
(a)   Figure 1.27 is a section across part of the valley shown in Figure 1.26. Make a copy of the section and label the following features:
(i)   larger fields on flat valley floor,
(ii)   broad terraces on gentle slopes,
(iii)   narrow terraces on steep slopes,
(iv)   cliff of bare rock,
(v)   steep slopes not cultivated.
(b)   Explain why the environment of Yemen leads to problems for farmers. Then describe how they have attempted to overcome these problems.
(c)   Two additional problems for farmers in this area are:
(i)   many fields are awkward shapes for efficient farming,
(ii)   falls of heavy rain on the bare slopes lead to problems on the fields below.
Explain these two problems.

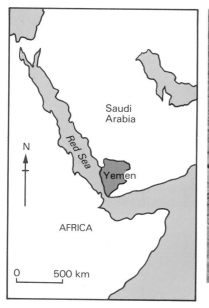

Fig. 1.25
Yemen

Fig. 1.26
Terraces in a valley in Yemen

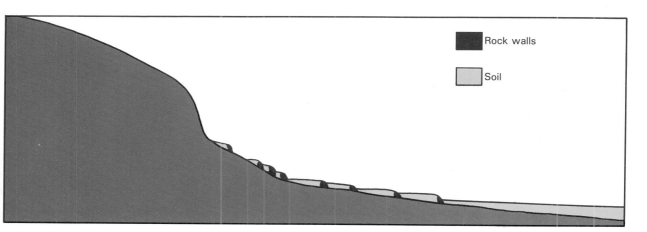

Rock walls

Soil

Fig. 1.27
Section across part of a valley in
Yemen

Summary

On the surface of the earth, there is a complex set of relationships between climate, relief, geology, soils, vegetation and animals. This set of relationships makes up the ecosystem. Water is the key to the ecosystem. The amount of rainfall falling in a year and its seasonal distribution will affect the type of vegetation in an area and thus man's choice of crops. Differences in temperature, relief and soil between areas will also have important influences on farming and on the distribution of man's settlements. In many areas the environment is difficult for man to live in and ways of overcoming problems such as steep slopes or lack of rainfall must be found.

2 Man in a rain forest environment

Fig. 2.1
Mean (average) rainfall and temperature for Singapore

In Chapter 1 we saw that those parts of the tropics with heavy rainfall and high temperatures throughout the year are usually covered with dense tropical rain forest. The climate graph for Singapore (Figure 2.1) shows the pattern of temperature and rainfall in such an area. Note that the conditions for each month are similar and that there are no clear seasons. The aerial photograph in Figure 2.2 shows the dense nature of the forest and gives some idea of the huge area it covers. The forest's structure in greater detail is shown in Figures 2.3 and 2.4.

Fig. 2.2

Fig. 2.3
Mangroves are found in coastal areas and along the sides of rivers. Note the stilt roots

Exercise 2.1
(a) Describe the general appearance of the forest, noting particularly the proportions of trees in each of the fairly distinct layers (Figure 2.4).
(b) Suggest why early explorers from Europe, who travelled along the rivers, believed that the forest was impossible to penetrate. Was their belief correct?

Fig. 2.4 Section through tropical rain forest

In Chapter 1 we saw that a large area of South America is covered by tropical rain forest (Figure 1.11). Most of this area has a very low density of population (on average a very small number of people live in each square kilometre). The hot, wet climate and the dense nature of the forest present problems for people living there and may deter people from other places moving into such an environment, especially as bacteria and insects causing disease thrive under hot, moist conditions. However, some areas of rain forest, for example in West Africa and southern Asia, have a greater population density. Here, perhaps, the natural problems are less severe or there are other positive factors encouraging people to live in such areas.

Amerindians

In the remoter parts of the Amazon Basin of South America, small tribes of Indians survive by hunting, fishing, collecting nuts and berries and by growing crops in small clearings in the forest.

Exercise 2.2

The class needs to be divided into three groups, the members of each group representing a different tribe—the Boros, the Secoyas and the Aguaranas.

(a) Put yourself in the place of a tribal group of about 30 people moving into an area. Study the information that your tribe has received from scouts about the area, as shown on your map and information table (Figures 2.7 and 2.8). The parts of the maps left blank are unknown territory for the tribe concerned. On your map you need to select the best of four possible sites for a village. To do this make a copy of the table in Figure 2.9 and give points for the various factors for each site. Instructions are given below the table on how to use it. The site with the highest total points is the best one for your group.

(b) Write a paragraph to explain the advantages of your chosen site.

Fig. 2.5 Indians of the Amazon Basin

Fig. 2.6 An Indian village in a forest clearing

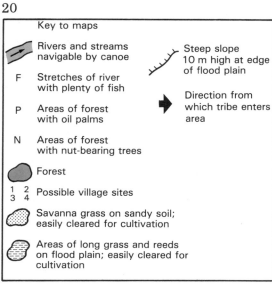

Key to maps

- Rivers and streams navigable by canoe
- F Stretches of river with plenty of fish
- P Areas of forest with oil palms
- N Areas of forest with nut-bearing trees
- Forest
- 1 2 / 3 4 Possible village sites
- Savanna grass on sandy soil; easily cleared for cultivation
- Areas of long grass and reeds on flood plain; easily cleared for cultivation
- Steep slope 10 m high at edge of flood plain
- Direction from which tribe enters area

Fig. 2.7

Group A—the Boros

1 km² 0 1 2 3 km

Group B—the Secoyas

1 km² 0 1 2 3 km

Group C—the Aguaranas

1 km² 0 1 2 3 km

Group A—The Boros

The Boros are moving upstream into the area. They live away from land which might be flooded and wish to be hidden in the forest for safety.
Diet: $\frac{1}{10}$ fish, $\frac{1}{10}$ oil palm fruits, $\frac{1}{10}$ nuts, $\frac{7}{10}$ crops (yams and cassava)
About 2 km² of land is needed for the next few years, although only a small patch is cleared each year.

Group B—The Secoyas

The Secoyas are moving downstream from the south-west into the area. They live near a river in huts built on poles to avoid flooding. Fishing is important.
Diet: $\frac{4}{10}$ fish, $\frac{1}{10}$ oil palm fruits, $\frac{1}{10}$ nuts, $\frac{4}{10}$ crops.
About 1 km² of land is needed for the next few years, although only a small patch is cleared each year.

Group C—The Aguaranas

The Aguaranas are moving downstream from the north-west into the area. They usually live near a river in huts built on poles, but sometimes live in a forest clearing. They are keen on hunting and fishing.
Diet: $\frac{1}{10}$ hunted animals (not included in table, as animals may be found all over the area), $\frac{3}{10}$ fish, $\frac{1}{10}$ oil palm fruits, $\frac{1}{10}$ nuts, $\frac{4}{10}$ crops.
About 1 km² of land is needed for the next few years, although only a small patch is cleared each year.
(Note: For the Aguaranas maximum points for food are 9 and for the total 14).

Fig. 2.8   *Fig. 2.9* ▶

Site	Food (10 points maximum)				Water (3)	Defence (2)	Total (15)
	Crops ( )	Oil palm fruits ( )	Nuts ( )	Fish ( )			
1							
2							
3							
4							

Tribe: _____

How to use the table
Take each site in turn and give it points for the various factors for each site. The maximum number of points for each factor is given in brackets. The maximum number of points for each type of food will depend on your tribe's diet. For example, the diet of the Boros is $\frac{7}{10}$ crops, $\frac{1}{10}$ oil palm fruits, $\frac{1}{10}$ nuts and $\frac{1}{10}$ fish, so the maximum points for the foods in this case will be 7 for crops and 1 for each of the other three types of foods. The site with the highest total points is the best one for your crop; put a ring round the total concerned.

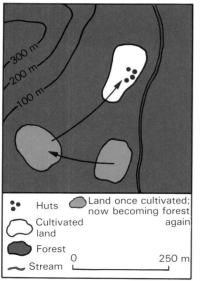

Fig. 2.10

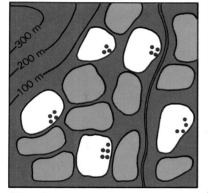

Fig. 2.11

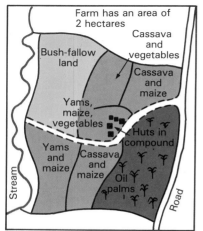

Fig. 2.12
Layout of a farm in eastern
Nigeria

On finding out from the other groups the sites they have chosen, two conclusions will stand out. Firstly, that the direction from which each tribe entered a new area had a bearing on choosing the possible sites for settlement. Secondly, the varying needs of the different tribes will have influenced the choice of settlement. Different needs give rise to different settlement patterns. Each tribe sees their forest surroundings in a different light.

The Indian tribes' farming system is a form of simple *subsistence cultivation*. They are providing for their own needs; they are not selling their produce to other people. Having made a clearing in the forest, they farm it for a few seasons only. Then, when the fertility of the soil has been used up, they move on and clear a new area of forest. Therefore, their method of farming is known as *shifting cultivation*.

Exercise 2.3
(a) Why does cultivation of the same piece of land for a few seasons make the land less fertile, so forcing a move onwards?
(b) When planting crops, ash from the burnt forest vegetation is spread on the land. How may this help?
(c) Large trees are not cut down and clearings are small. How may this help the soil in an area of heavy rainfall?
(d) Shifting cultivation wastes an important resource. It is only possible in a large area with few people. Explain these two statements.

Population pressure

One of the areas of tropical rain forest with a relatively high density of population is West Africa (see Figure 1.13). Shifting cultivation was practised in these areas in the past but as the population grew, it could no longer provide enough food. The system therefore had to be modified.

Exercise 2.4
(a) Figure 2.10 shows an area of tropical rain forest with a low density of population. After 4 years, the village is moved and new plots are cultivated. Copy the map, add the position of the new village and plots, which must be in forest land not used before, labelling all features. Head the map *Shifting Cultivation*.
(b) Figure 2.11 shows an area of tropical rain forest with a much greater density of population. There are five villages in the same area as in Figure 2.10. It is clear that after four years, there will not be enough room for all the settlements to be moved and new plots to be cut out of untouched forest. Under the heading *Bush Fallowing* say where the people will be forced to find land for their crops in the area of the map. Then say whether the villages will move position or not. If they will not move, explain why. Suggest why the land will suffer and crop yields may possibly become lower.

Bush fallowing involves letting land rest for just a few years before being cultivated again. While it is resting, it will be overgrown by young trees and shrubs or 'bush'. It is a system of farming used widely in Africa, where there is population pressure on the land. Figure 2.12 shows a typical farm layout in eastern Nigeria. Not all farms form a compact unit like this one. In some parts of West Africa the farmers

Fig. 2.13
Cassava

live in villages and the land of the different villagers is jumbled up together. Some of the crops grown on the farm in Figure 2.12 are shown in Figure 1.15: cassava, an important root crop is shown in Figure 2.13. Notice that crops are often grown together in the small fields. One crop can protect the soil from erosion by heavy rain as the other is growing.

Exercise 2.5

(a) Which crops grown on the farm in Figure 2.12 are (i) root crops, (ii) grain crops?

(b) Although tropical rain forests have rain throughout the year, eastern Nigeria receives most of its rain between May and October. Planting is mainly done in the drier period, harvesting from June onwards. Explain this pattern of work.

(c) Figure 2.14 shows bush fallowing in West Africa. Another example of bush fallowing is shown in the photograph of oil palms in Figure 1.15. (Notice the bush growing beneath the oil palms.) What other work do these photographs suggest will be necessary with bush fallowing?

Cash crops

Most of the crops grown on farms in eastern Nigeria are subsistence crops, grown for feeding the farmer's own family, although if there is a small surplus it may be sold in the market of a nearby town. Palm oil, however, is produced for sale either to a palm oil mill or to traders in the local market, with the farmer using just a limited amount as cooking oil. It is therefore known as a *cash crop*. The money from its sale will partly be put back into the farm but also allows private spending by the farmer.

Fig. 2.14
Bush fallowing—a farmer weeding and building up yam mounds in Nigeria. The stems of last year's crop (sorghum, a grain crop) have been bent over for the yam plants to climb up

Fig. 2.15
Farming seen as a system

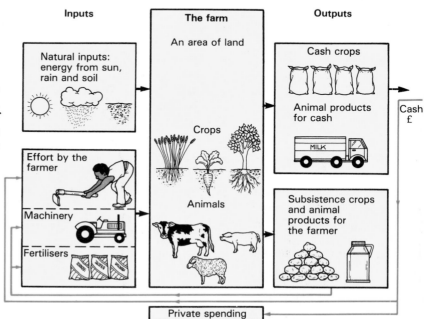

In Chapter 1 we looked at the relationships which exist between climate, relief, geology, soil, water and the activities of man. The network of relationships was a system. Farming itself is a system.

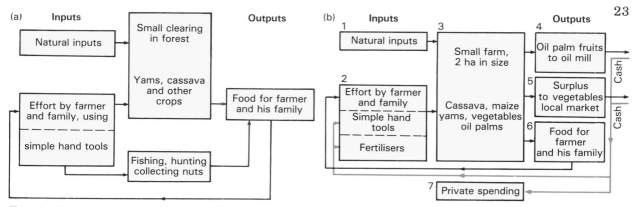

Fig. 2.16
Systems diagrams
(a) Shifting agriculture in the Amazon Basin
(b) Farming in eastern Nigeria

The effort put in by the farmer and energy from the sun, rain and soil are the *inputs*; the crops the farmers produce are the *outputs*. The diagram in Figure 2.15 summarises this idea. The idea of a system can be applied to different types of farm and make it easier to compare one type of farming with another. Figure 2.16 show the systems of (a) the South American Indian shifting cultivator and (b) the Nigerian peasant farmer.

(a) Plantation agriculture

(b) Open-cast mining for iron ore

(c) Felling timber

Fig. 2.17

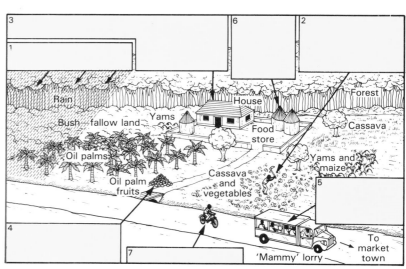

Fig. 2.18
A farm in eastern Nigeria

Fig. 2.19
The usefulness of forests for timber production
(a) Section through tropical rain forest, West Africa
(b) Section through coniferous forest, Finland

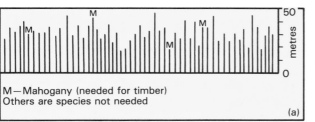

M—Mahogany (needed for timber)
Others are species not needed

(a)

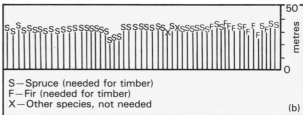

S—Spruce (needed for timber)
F—Fir (needed for timber)
X—Other species, not needed

(b)

Furniture

Plywood

Veneers

Thin sheet of hardwood (a veneer) glued onto base

Base of low-cost chipboard

Mahogany

Fig. 2.20
Some uses of tropical hardwoods

Major changes in the environment

So far, we have seen how man uses the rain forest environment on a fairly simple level. Figure 2.17 shows how man might have a much more marked effect on this environment.

These newer and more complex activities of man are the result of demands for the resources of the rain forests from people who live outside these areas. Clearly the major effect on the environment is the removal of the forest. Also, the way of life of people living in these areas will be affected, not always for the best. We shall take a closer look in later chapters at plantations, which are huge farms producing export crops, and the production of minerals.

Timber production

The most obvious resource of the tropical rain forest is timber. Clearly, there will be problems of felling timber and getting it out of the forest in remote, less-developed parts of the world. However, one of the main problems is the nature of the forest itself. In any forest, not all species or types of tree may be suitable for use. Also, only trees which have reached a reasonable size will be worth cutting down. The diagrams in Figure 2.19 show sections through typical small areas of (a) tropical rain forest in West Africa, and (b) coniferous forest in Finland.

Timber resources	Extent of forests is shown on the map. Okoumé is the most important timber. Areas of okoumé near the coast have been cleared and re-planting is taking place, but 50 years will pass before important timber is produced.
Importance of timber as an export	£57 million in 1974; 21% of Gabon's exports.
Transport	The hilly and forested nature of the country makes railway and road building difficult and so timber is transported mostly by floating logs down rivers. Logs can be towed in rafts along the coast. Logs and plywood can be carried on the railway, or at a higher cost, by road.
Port facilities for export	At Owendo and Pointe Noire (Congo) large ships can tie up at quays and be loaded directly from the land. At Libreville and Port Gentil cargo must be taken by small boats to ships anchored offshore. Quays for large ships are being built at Port Gentil.
Population and main towns (for labour supply)	Gabon has a population of only 530 000 and has a low average density of population. Main towns: Libreville (251 400 people), Port Gentil (77 100), Lambaréné (22 700). Other towns on the map are all very small.
Electricity supply	Hydro-electric power stations near Libreville and Franceville. Power stations using oil at Libreville and Port Gentil. Elsewhere, electricity supplies are not enough for a factory and new power stations would have to be built.

Fig. 2.22
Gabon: information table

Despite natural disadvantages, the tropical rain forests produce hardwoods, which are in great demand because of the fine finishes that they can give to furniture and because of their strength. Figure 2.20 shows some important uses of these woods which will obtain high prices. In fact, one reason that many of the rain forest species are of little use to the timber companies is that they could not obtain a high enough price to pay for the work involved in getting the trees out.

A country in which the felling and export of timber is of great importance is Gabon in West Africa (Figure 2.21). Almost all the country is densely forested. The forests contain most of the world's reserves of okoumé, used for high quality plywood, and valuable amounts of mahogany and ebony. Until the 1970s, timber was the country's most important export. While large amounts of timber are still exported, oil has now become the leading export.

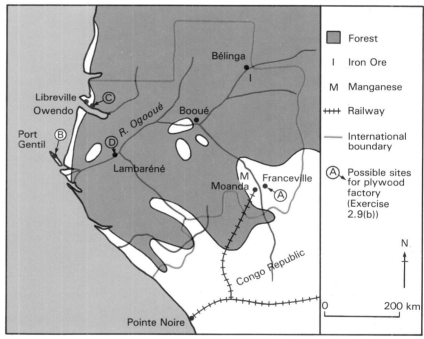

Fig. 2.21
Gabon

Exercise 2.8

(a) Look at an atlas vegetation map of Africa and compare it with a map showing the countries of Africa. Suggest why Gabon has greater advantages of position as a timber producer and exporter than (i) Nigeria, and (ii) Zaire.

(b) Study the map of Gabon in Figure 2.21 and the information table on the timber industry and other aspects of the country (Figure 2.22). Imagine that you are responsible for deciding on the best place in Gabon to build a factory making plywood for export. Copy the table in Figure 2.23, which includes a list of the factors you have to consider when deciding where to build the factory. Award marks to each possible location for each of these factors. The location with the highest total of marks is the best. Write a paragraph to explain the advantages of the location you have chosen.

Requirements of the plywood factory	Maximum points	Sites			
		A	B	C	D
A good position for receiving a large and continuous supply of timber	20				
Port facilities for export or good rail links to port	12				
Labour supply	5				
Electricity supply	3				
Totals					

Fig. 2.23

Country	Value of timber exports (£ million) (1974)	Value of other exports (£ million) (1974)
Gabon	57	272
Nigeria	10	5084
Zaire	4	764
Cameroon	33	232
Ghana	51	306
Ivory Coast	146	529

Fig. 2.24 Timber exports of some African countries

The export of hardwoods is very important for Gabon and some other countries. Developing countries need to export their resources such as timber so as to bring in money to buy manufactured goods from other countries.

Exercise 2.9

(a) Because timber and oil account for so much of the export earnings of Gabon, the government has tried to develop the growing of cash crops and the mining of iron ore and manganese. Explain why the development and export of minerals is less easy than the development of timber and requires huge amounts of money. (The map of Gabon may give you some ideas.)

(b) To develop the minerals, a railway is under construction from Owendo through Booué to Bélinga. A branch will run from Booué to Franceville and Moanda. Look at the map to see where these new railways run.

(i) How may they help the timber industry?

(ii) If the plywood factory was being built after these lines had been finished, would you have chosen a different location?

(c) Suggest why the felling of timber has to be carefully controlled, with a limit being placed on the account of timber to be cut down in each area. (See Figure 2.22.)

Exercise 2.10

(a) Figure 2.24 shows the value of timber exported by several African countries together with the total value of their other exports. Draw a bar graph to show these figures. Give each country two bars, one for timber and the other for the other exports.

(b) Say how your answer to Exercise 2.8(a) might explain the patterns shown on your bar graph.

The Trans-Amazonica Highway

The largest area of tropical forest in the world is in the Amazon Basin of South America; most of this area is part of Brazil. Brazil has attempted to open up and develop the Amazon Basin by the construction of major new roads, the most important being the Trans-Amazonica Highway, begun in 1971. Previously, the Amazon itself and its tributaries had been the area's only outlet. Figure 2.25 shows the new roads and the main navigable rivers.

In order to study the transport network of this area easily, distances between points on the network have been shown. Two types of

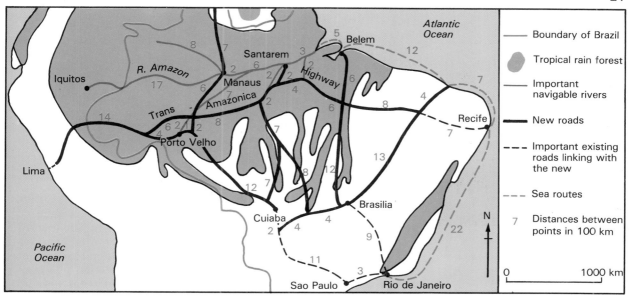

Fig. 2.25
The Amazon Basin

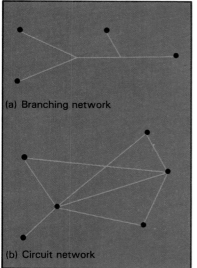

Fig. 2.26
Two types of network
(a) Branching network
(b) Circuit network

network are shown in Figure 2.26: branching network and a circuit network, in which routes join and separate. With the construction of the new roads, the type of transport network in the Amazon Basin has changed from the simple branching network (the river and its major tributaries) to a more complex circuit network. Also, movement along the roads will be quicker than by boat along the river.

Exercise 2.11

(a) One of the reasons for the new roads was to connect Amazonia with the densely populated areas of Brazil to the south. To examine how the accessibility of the few Amazonian towns has been improved, we can compare *detour indices* between places before and after the building of the new roads. If a route does not follow a straight line between two points it connects, it is making a detour.

$$\text{A Detour Index} = \frac{\text{Actual distance}}{\text{Straight line distance}} \times 100$$

An index of 100 would mean a route followed the straight line and did not deviate from it at all. From the map, calculate the detour indices for Manaus to Brasilia, the new capital of Brazil:
(i) by river, sea and previously existing roads, via Rio de Janeiro;
(ii) by the new roads.
Fill in your results on a copy of the table in Figure 2.27.

	Straight line distance	Distance by route available before new roads	Distance by new roads	Detour index before new roads	Detour index after new roads
Manaus to Brasilia					
Porto Velho to Belem					

Fig. 2.27

28

Fig. 2.28
Road construction in the Amazon Basin

1 To improve transport links between the towns of Amazonia and the rest of Brazil.

2 To shorten travelling times within Amazonia.

3 To develop new farming areas which will produce crops for export.

4 To encourage the growth of towns in Amazonia.
(The towns will become market centres for the farming regions).

5 To bring the Indians of Amazonia into the 20th century by providing education, medical care and jobs.

Fig. 2.29
Aims of the new roads in Amazonia

(b) Calculate detour indices for Porto Velho to Belem, both places within Amazonia:
(i) by river,
(ii) by the new roads.
Again, put your results in the table.
(c) Look at the map and the table you have completed. Have the new roads had a greater effect on improving links between Amazonia and the rest of Brazil or between towns within Amazonia? By how many times has the accessibility of Manaus to Brasilia been improved?

The new roads in Amazonia have been difficult to construct. Figur 2.28 gives some idea of the problems. Other difficulties have bee getting equipment into the area in the first place, and the hazard c tropical diseases. New farms have been established along the road and occupied mainly by people from the poor, densely-populate north-east of Brazil. These people face many problems. The land i difficult to clear; soils are of poor quality for cultivation year afte year. Even with the new roads, markets for their produce ar thousands of miles away. The people require training in farmin; methods and take time in adjusting to life in the hot, wet climate

The Indians already living in Amazonia, following the way of lif we looked at earlier in this chapter, find that to meet up with . 'developed' way of life is a great shock. As a result of the opening up o Amazonia with new roads, they will have to deal with money, ne customs, and different languages. They may not be resistant to dis eases brought in by the newcomers. Some of the people involved i developing Amazonia have tricked and even killed the Indians. Man Indians end up poverty-stricken and unemployed in the Amazonia towns.

Exercise 2.12
(a) Look at Figure 2.28. Suggest why road construction in Amazonia is very difficult.
(b) Figure 2.29 lists the main aims of the new roads in Amazonia. Which of the aims have been achieved? Which of the aims have not been achieved? Explain why.

Summary

This chapter started by looking at the relationship between the rain forest environment and man with traditional, rather primitive ways of using it. The fact that such ways have survived so long shows that they have been largely successful in making use of the difficult environment. We then saw how this simple way of life may change, through increasing population pressures and the introduction of cash crops.

More drastic changes will take place in both people's way of life and in the environment itself when modern large-scale developments such as mining, forestry or road construction take place. Such developments may not have the desired effect of improvement, and interference with one part of the natural system may have bad effects on another part.

3 Man in areas affected by drought

One of the least attractive environments for man to live in is an area with very little or no rainfall. An area such as this will clearly be unsuitable for growing crops unless water is available from wells or rivers; possibilities for livestock grazing will be very limited as well. There are, however, widespread areas with dry conditions for only part of the year and/or with a small amount of rainfall, allowing cultivation to a limited extent. Such areas are described as having a *semi-arid* environment.

Figure 3.1 gives the monthly means of temperature and rainfall for Kayes in Mali, West Africa. The figures are typical of a tropical semi-arid location.

Fig. 3.1
Mean monthly rainfall and temperature figures for Kayes, Mali

Exercise 3.1

(a) Using the figures in Figure 3.1 draw a climatic graph for Kayes, arranged like the graph in Figure 2.1. Bracket together those months with less than 50 mm of rainfall and those with over 50 mm of rainfall, and label them 'dry season' and 'wet season' respectively.

(b) In Britain, we distinguish our seasons quite differently. What is the way in which we distinguish our seasons? Why would this not be a suitable way for Kayes?

	J	F	M	A	M	J	J	A	S	O	N	D
Temperature (°C)	26	28	31	34	36	36	33	30	28	30	30	27
Rainfall (mm)	0	0	0	5	20	92	190	195	150	52	10	8

In Chapter 1 we saw that the tropical areas of South America and Africa with contrasting dry and wet seasons were generally covered with savanna vegetation (Figure 3.2). Much of the ground is covered with grass, but scattered trees are also present. Strictly speaking, only the savanna areas on the fringes of the desert with a very long dry season like Kayes are truly semi-arid. In this chapter, however, we will be looking at examples of man's activities in areas where the dry season is shorter as well, because drought is a problem to be overcome throughout the savannas.

Fig. 3.2 Savanna

Wildlife and drought

The problem of drought must be overcome by plants and animals in the natural ecosystem too. Adaptations must be made by both if they are to survive the dry season.

Figure 3.3 shows herds of herbivores (plant-eating animals) grazing on the savanna grasslands of East Africa. Large herds of antelopes, zebras and wildebeests once grazed most of Africa's savannas. Now, because of the pressure of man's activities, they are found in large numbers only in areas set aside as national parks or conservation areas.

Let us see how these animals adapt to the semi-arid environment. Figure 3.4 shows the distribution of rainfall and animal migration routes in northern Tanzania, East Africa. The wetter areas tend to be

Fig. 3.3

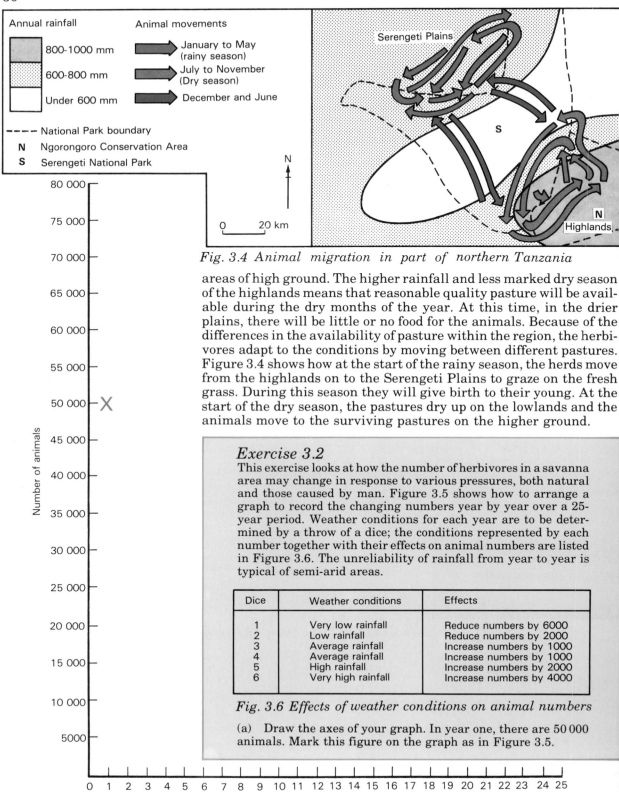

Fig. 3.4 *Animal migration in part of northern Tanzania*

areas of high ground. The higher rainfall and less marked dry season of the highlands means that reasonable quality pasture will be available during the dry months of the year. At this time, in the drier plains, there will be little or no food for the animals. Because of the differences in the availability of pasture within the region, the herbivores adapt to the conditions by moving between different pastures. Figure 3.4 shows how at the start of the rainy season, the herds move from the highlands on to the Serengeti Plains to graze on the fresh grass. During this season they will give birth to their young. At the start of the dry season, the pastures dry up on the lowlands and the animals move to the surviving pastures on the higher ground.

Exercise 3.2

This exercise looks at how the number of herbivores in a savanna area may change in response to various pressures, both natural and those caused by man. Figure 3.5 shows how to arrange a graph to record the changing numbers year by year over a 25-year period. Weather conditions for each year are to be determined by a throw of a dice; the conditions represented by each number together with their effects on animal numbers are listed in Figure 3.6. The unreliability of rainfall from year to year is typical of semi-arid areas.

Dice	Weather conditions	Effects
1	Very low rainfall	Reduce numbers by 6000
2	Low rainfall	Reduce numbers by 2000
3	Average rainfall	Increase numbers by 1000
4	Average rainfall	Increase numbers by 1000
5	High rainfall	Increase numbers by 2000
6	Very high rainfall	Increase numbers by 4000

Fig. 3.6 *Effects of weather conditions on animal numbers*

(a) Draw the axes of your graph. In year one, there are 50 000 animals. Mark this figure on the graph as in Figure 3.5.

Fig. 3.5 *Changing animal numbers over 25 years in a savanna area*

(b) For years 2 to 7 in turn, throw the dice, look up the weather conditions and their effects on animal numbers, calculate the number of animals remaining, and plot the figure on the graph. For example, if in year 2 a 1 was thrown, numbers would be reduced by 6000 and so 44 000 animals would remain.

(c) An increasing amount of land is being used for cultivation or cattle grazing by man. Conflict with man also means an increase in hunting. For each year from 8 to 15, continue to throw the dice as before, adjusting the numbers of animals, but also reduce the number by 2000 each year to represent the increasing pressures due to man's use of the land.

(d) In order to maintain the animal numbers, a National Park is created in the area not yet farmed. Hunting is banned but poachers kill animals for their skins. For years 16 to 20, continue to throw the dice for weather conditions but now deduct an additional 1000 each year to represent the loss as a result of poaching.

(e) The government has carried out a campaign against the cattle disease known as *rinderpest*. The campaign has also reduced the effect of the disease on wild herbivores. For years 21 to 25, continue to throw the dice for weather conditions but now *add* 1000 each year to represent the increasing numbers. (The gain due to rinderpest control more than offsets poaching losses).

Exercise 3.3

Consider the changes in numbers shown on your graph and then answer the following questions:

(a) Without interference by man, as in years 1 to 8, what is the general trend in the number of animals?

(b) Why would cultivation and cattle grazing be expanding? Suggest why this would lead to decreasing numbers of wild animals.

(c) The main reason for the creation of a National Park is to conserve wild life. Suggest how it could benefit the economy of a relatively poor African country.

(d) Even with the creation of a National Park, numbers of animals may decline. Suggest how the problems of (i) dry years (ii) poaching could be overcome. What problems do your suggested methods raise?

Fig. 3.7
Plants adapted to drought
(a) The Baobab tree stores water in its thick trunk. It has small leathery leaves to prevent loss of water. It is deciduous, losing its leaves in the dry season

(b) The Acacia tree has long tap roots to reach water well below the surface. It has small leaves and is deciduous, losing its leaves in the dry season

(c) Grasses lie dormant and have a scorched appearance in the dry season. When rain comes they grow rapidly, flower and seed

Plants and drought

Plants, as with animals, need to adapt to semi-arid conditions. The problem is to survive the dry season. To do this, plants may:
1. store water,
2. prevent water loss (by reducing transpiration),
3. tap water well below the surface,
4. remain dormant (not growing) in the dry season, sometimes surviving only as seeds which germinate when rain falls.

Figure 3.7 shows some savanna plants adapted to drought in different ways.

Exercise 3.4

Figure 3.8 is an outline table designed to summarise the ways in which the plants pictured in Figure 3.7 adapt to drought. Copy the table and fill it in by studying Figure 3.7. Where methods of adaptation do not apply to a particular plant, enter dashes in the table. The table has already been completed for the Baobab tree.

	Water storage	Preventing water loss	Tapping water at depth	Remaining dormant in dry season
Baobab tree	Stores water in thick trunk	Small, leathery leaves; loses leaves in dry season	—	—
Acacia tree				
Grasses				

Fig. 3.8
How savanna plants adapt to drought

Fig. 3.9

Some savanna grassland areas with a shorter dry season were once forested, but the action of man and animals has either destroyed or prevented tree growth. By setting fire to the vegetation, young trees are destroyed and grass suitable for grazing animals will spring up. Wild animals may destroy trees as well (Figure 3.9).

Nomads

The need for animals and plants to adapt to drought in semi-arid areas suggests that man's activities must also adapt to the environment. The traditional pattern of livestock 'farming' in such areas is called *nomadism*, a system in which herds are moved across wide areas in search of pasture. Cultivation must involve plants which are either adapted to drought or can be grown within the rainy season, unless there is a supply of water available for irrigation.

Fig. 3.10 (above-left)
A Nuer tribesman and his bull
Fig. 3.11 (above-right)
A Nuer cattle camp. In the background there is a boat on the River Sobat

In the southern Sudan in north-east Africa, there are many *nomadic pastoralists* who keep large herds of poor quality, hump-backed Zebu cattle (Figures 3.10 and 3.11). In the driest areas, sheep and goats are also kept. A man's wealth is judged on the number of cattle he owns, so the animals are killed for meat or hides only when old and thin, and well after the cows have stopped producing milk. Vegetables and grain are obtained by bartering with cultivators. In the drier part of the area, north of the Bahr el Arab river (see Figure 3.12), Arab tribes move their animals between wet-season pastures on the open savanna and the dry-season pastures further south near the river. They are forced to make the movement south in the dry season because pasture on the open savanna becomes unusable and water holes dry up. Pasture survives only near the river.

Further south live negro tribes such as the Nuer. Their movement is more complex and is due to:

1. the need to find pasture and water in the dry season,
2. the need to avoid areas flooded in the wet season,
3. the need to avoid areas infested by the tsetse fly in the wet season. (The tsetse fly spreads the fatal cattle disease known as trypanosomiasis or sleeping sickness.)

From May onwards, in the wet season, much of the area in which the Nuer live is flooded by the Bahr el Jebel (the Nile) and the Sobat and so they move to ridges or islands of slightly higher land. They cannot move to the large areas of higher ground in the south-east because of the tsetse fly menace there. When the floodwaters retreat in the dry season, grass springs up on the clay plains. Near the rivers it lasts right through the dry season. However, as the clay plains dry out, water holes begin to dry up, as do some of the rivers, so survival towards the end of the dry season is always a problem.

Exercise 3.5

(a) Describe the appearance of the nomad's home shown in the left background of Figure 3.11. Why is it of such makeshift appearance? In what season was the photograph taken? Give a reason for your answer.

(b) Describe how the Sudanese nomads' view of the importance of their cattle differs from that of European farmers.

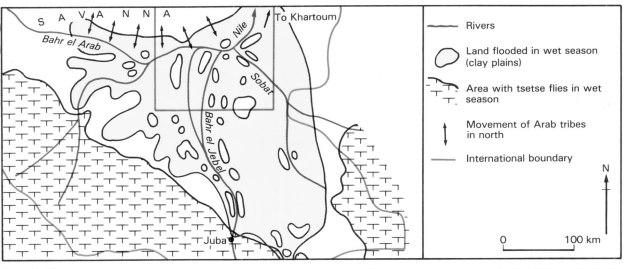

Fig. 3.12
Southern Sudan

Exercise 3.6

Make an enlarged copy of that part of Figure 3.12 outlined by the rectangle. On your map, put in arrows in different colours to represent:

(i) movement of the Arab tribes in the north of the area (already marked on Figure 3.12).

(ii) movement of the negro tribes between islands of high ground and the surrounding clay plains.

(iii) movement of surplus cattle to market (northwards by boat along the Bahr el Jebel or Nile to Khartoum, the capital of the Sudan). Add a key to your map.

Fig. 3.13
A drought scene near Timbuctu, Mali. Notice the lack of grass, resulting from drought and overgrazing

Fig. 3.15
A water-hole near Timbuctu. Many such water-holes dried up in the drought of the early 1970s

When the rains fail

Drought is a problem to be overcome every year by cattle herders of semi-arid areas. However, a characteristic of semi-arid areas is the unreliability of rainfall; rainfall may be particularly low and the dry season longer than normal for several years in succession. For several years up to 1973, rainfall totals were extremely low in the drier parts of the African savanna known as the Sahel zone (Figure 3.14).

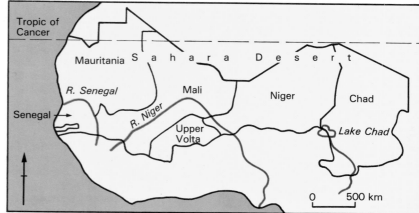

Fig. 3.14 The Sahel countries

As a result, the very limited amount of available pasture was quickly used up and about 7 million cattle (one-third of the total number in the Sahel countries) died through lack of food and water (Figures 3.13 and 3.15). Farmers were also affected. Not enough water for irrigating crops could be obtained from the Niger and Senegal rivers, and Lake Chad shrank in size. 100 000 people died in the famine despite aid from richer countries.

Exercise 3.7

(a) Make a copy of the map of the Sahel countries shown in Figure 3.14. On your map, draw bars using a scale of 1 cm to 1 000 000 cattle on each Sahel country to show the changes in cattle numbers caused by the severe drought. (Figure 3.16 gives details of cattle numbers). Also on your map, label the other effects of the drought. Give your map a suitable title and a key to explain the bars as in Figure 3.17.

| Country | Size of cattle herd | |
	1972	1973
Senegal	2 500 000	2 200 000
Mauritania	2 300 000	1 600 000
Mali	5 000 000	3 300 000
Upper Volta	2 600 000	2 200 000
Niger	4 200 000	2 700 000
Chad	4 700 000	3 000 000

Fig. 3.16

(b) Figure 3.18 shows some developments which have taken place in the Sahel since 1973. Look at these photographs and their captions, and then explain how the new developments will help the cattle herders and farmers of the Sahel.

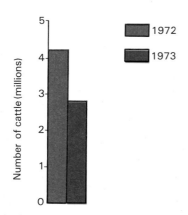

Fig. 3.17

(a)

(d)

(b)

(c)

(e)

(f)

Fig. 3.18
(a) A small dam in Mauritania, built across a water course in which a stream flows only after a rainstorm
(b) Cattle in Mauritania being vaccinated against cattle-pest in a new concrete cattle dip. Healthy cattle result in better quality meat and hides
(c) Downstream of dams such as the one in Photograph (a), irrigated crops can be grown. This is a crop of millet

(d) A new well in Mauritania. It has a deep concrete-lined shaft
(e) Mobile petrol-driven pumps being used to pump water from the River Niger on to crops of rice
(f) The fishing industry is being developed along the River Niger in Mali

Conflict with farmers

In many semi-arid areas, an increasing amount of land is being cultivated by permanently settled people. This is due both to an increase in the population (therefore more food must be grown) and the wish of the farmers to grow cash crops. Thus less pasture is available for livestock herders.

Both drought and loss of land to cultivation leads to every bit of available pasture being used up. Grass is eaten right down to the roots and bare soil is exposed. This is known as *overgrazing* (Figure 3.13). In dry periods, wind blows the soil away and in the rainy season, heavy downpours wash it away. Thus large areas of grassland have been affected by *soil erosion* (Figure 3.19).

In some semi-arid areas, governments have decided that the use of land by nomadic pastoralists is wasteful, and that the land could produce more if tribes lived in permanent villages, practised cultivation besides livestock rearing, and learnt more advanced methods of farming. This is so with the Masai people, who live in Kenya and Tanzania in East Africa (Figure 3.20). Much of the land they used to move over has now been used for cultivation by other groups of

Fig. 3.19
Soil eroded by rapidly flowing water after heavy downpours

36

Fig. 3.20
Masai

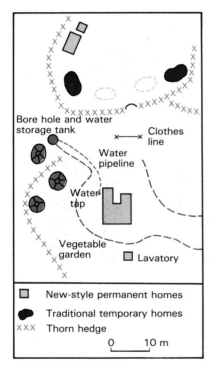

Fig. 3.21
A Masai manyatta

people. Their movement has therefore been restricted and the pastures left to them have been overgrazed. While some Masai follow their traditional way of life, others have changed their way of life to some degree. Figure 3.21 shows a Masai settlement or manyatta. It consists of some traditional homes surrounded by a thorn hedge to keep out lions, but also some modern-style homes and water-storage tank supplied by a bore-hole.

> ### Exercise 3.8
> (a) Explain why an increasing population of farmers is a problem for nomad cattle herders.
> (b) The number of Masai and their cattle has increased during the twentieth century. What effects would this have had on the pastures?

Cultivation in semi-arid areas

In Exercise 1.6, we saw that climatic conditions may restrict the growing of crops to particular climatic zones. In an area with a dry season, unless irrigation is used, the farmer is forced to grow crops which, like the wild plants, are either adapted to survive drought or will grow within the space of the wet season. Even with irrigation, trees such as rubber or cocoa cannot be grown as they need humid air. On the other hand, a crop such as cotton likes a short dry season and could not be grown in a rain forest environment. It is when the season of drought is particularly long that the variety of crops from which a farmer may make his choice is very limited.

The unreliability of rainfall in semi-arid areas leads to severe problems for cultivation. Figure 3.22 lists some important subsistence and cash crops grown by farmers in an area known as the Miombo Woodlands in central Tanzania. The table also shows how both the yields of the subsistence crops in terms of food value they give and profits from the cash crops vary according to rainfall amounts. Figure 3.23 shows how a large family's fields are arranged in the Miombo Woodlands. The crops are grown in small fields cut out of the bush. With the exception of the rice, crops are changed or rotated from year to year. After several years of cultivation, a field is left fallow for about 4 years before being used again. The rice requires

		Wet year	Average year	Dry year
Yields of subsistence crops in terms of food value (see note below)	Maize	60	55	50
	Cassava	15	30	40
	Rice	65	55	35
	Yams	80	45	10
Profits from cash crops for one field	Tobacco	£65	£60	£35
	Sunflowers	£60	£55	£45

The subsistence crops

The yield of these crops is in terms of their calorific value, that is the amount of energy they give. Protein is also necessary for a balanced diet. Both maize and cassava are low in protein. Rice and yams have a higher protein content. Cassava can be left in the ground for two years and so forms a famine reserve.

Fig. 3.22
How yields of subsistence crops and profits from cash crops vary with weather conditions

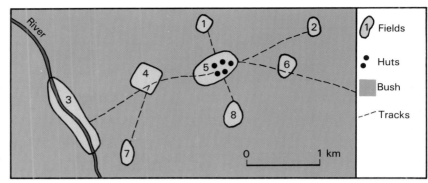

Fig. 3.23
Farming in the Miombo Woodlands, Tanzania

thorough irrigation and so is always grown by the river. The other
crops grown, with the exception of the cassava, are irrigated from
small streams for part of the dry season, but in the dry years there is
often not enough water for this.

Exercise 3.9
(a)   On a copy of the map shown in Figure 3.23, allocate a crop to
each of the fields except for one, which will be left fallow. You
must have at least one field of each crop. No more than two fields
should be used for cash crops. Remember that the rice field needs
plenty of irrigation water.
(b)   Describe how the fields are arranged in relation to:
(i)   the huts, (ii) the river.
Explain your answers.
(c)   Refer to Figure 3.22. Suggest why the farmer chooses to
grow cassava as one of his crops.
(d)   Suggest why the farmer rotates his crops and also leaves
each field fallow for about 4 years.

Field number	Year 1		Year 2		Year 3		Year 4		Year 5		Year 6		Year 7		Year 8	
	Crop choice	Yield or profit	Crop choice	Yield or profit	Crop choice	Yield or profit	Crop choice	Yield or profit	Crop choice	Yield or profit	Crop choice	Yield or profit	Crop choice	Yield of profit	Crop choice	Yield or profit
1 2 3 4 5 6 7 8																
Type of weather																
Total yield of subsistence crops																
Total profit from cash crops																

Fig. 3.24

Dice	Weather conditions
1	Dry
2	Dry
3	Average
4	Average
5	Wet
6	Wet

Fig. 3.25
Dice numbers and weather conditions

Field number	Year 1		
	Crop choice	Yield or profit	
1	Y	45	
2	M	55	
3	R	55	
4	M	55	
5	T	£60	
6	S	£55	
7	C	30	
8	Fallow	0	
Type of weather	Average		
Total yield of subsistence crops	240		
Total profit from cash crops	£115		

Key M Maize Y Yams
  C Cassava T Tobacco
  R Rice S Sunflowers

Fig. 3.26
A completed column

Exercise 3.10

(a) Make a copy of the table in Figure 3.24. Enter the choice of crops you made for each field in Exercise 3.9 in the Year 1 column.

(b) In order to find out the weather experienced in Year 1, throw a dice. The type of weather indicated by each number on the dice is shown in Figure 3.25. Then work out the crop yield (for subsistence crops) or profit (for cash crops) for each field, from the information in Figure 3.23. Also calculate the total yields and profits for the whole year; Figure 3.26 shows how a column may appear for an average year.

(c) Now continue from Year 2 to Year 8, each year making your crop choice and then seeing what the weather will be. Observe the following points:

(i) the rice will always be in the same field; only one field should be used for rice,

(ii) other crops must not be grown in the same field two years in succession,

(iii) at least one field of each subsistence crop must be grown (variety is necessary for a balanced diet),

(iv) no more than two fields of cash crops may be grown,

(v) the field left fallow in Year 1 should stay fallow in Years 2, 3 and 4; another field will be fallow from Years 5 to 8.

Exercise 3.11

Look at the results of Exercise 3.9 and then answer the following questions:

(a) If yields in an average year are sufficient to feed the farmer's family, what problems will a farmer have in producing subsistence crops in an area of unreliable rainfall?

(b) Besides being essential for a balanced diet, why does the farmer grow a variety of crops?

(c) What would be the effect of a regular supply of irrigation water each year on the farmer's land?

Patterns of land use

The patterns of land use we have just looked at involved just an isolated family's holding. Figure 3.27 shows the pattern of land use on a larger scale in a savanna area; around the village of Soba in northern Nigeria. Land near the village is always cultivated, crops

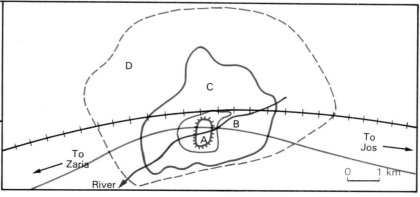

Key

+―+ Railway
― Main road
― Boundary of land-use zones
ᴜᴜᴜ Village walls (contain cultivated land besides houses)
---- Boundary of Soba land
A B ⎰ Different land use zones
C D ⎱ Village is in zone A

Fig. 3.27
Land-use zones around the village of Soba, northern Nigeria

being fertilised with the manure of animals kept within the village walls. In the zone furthest from the village, bush fallowing as in the tropical rain forests, is practised. The key to the arrangement of the land-use zones is the amount of labour the different land uses need. Figure 3.28 gives details of the types of land use found in this area and of the work necessary on each type.

Land use	How the soil is kept fertile	Work needed
Sorghum, cotton and groundnuts	Bush fallowing	Clearing bush; crops visited for planting, some weeding and harvesting
Vegetables, spices and tobacco	Manure from animals kept in village	Daily visits to pick vegetables and spices. Frequent cultivation and manure spreading.
Bush; very little land cultivated (only near isolated groups of huts)	—	—
Sorghum, tobacco, and cotton	Some manure used. Crops rotated.	Crops visited for planting, manuring and harvesting. Tobacco needs careful attention.

Fig. 3.28
Soba: land-use types and work needed

Fig. 3.29
Sorghum or Guinea Corn

Exercise 3.12
Figure 3.31 represents the land-use zones around Soba in the form of concentric circles.
(a)   Make a copy of the diagram in Figure 3.31 and shade each zone in a different colour. Decide which zone is used for each type of land use by considering the information in Figure 3.28, and so make a key for your diagram.
(b)   About one-fifth of the bush-fallow zone is cultivated in any one year. Mark off and label one-fifth of this zone on your diagram (as in Figure 3.30) and put bush symbols over the colouring in the remaining four-fifths of the zone.

Your completed diagram should show that the most *intensive* land use is near the houses (a large amount of work is needed and the value of produce per hectare is high) and that the most *extensive* land use is furthest from the village (a small amount of work is needed and the value of produce per hectare is low).

Exercise 3.13
(a)   Rewrite the definitions of intensive and extensive land use, but expand each one by using the examples from the village we have studied.
(b)   Explain why permanent cultivation is possible in some zones but bush fallowing is necessary in one.
(c)   If distance from the village was the only factor involved in influencing the pattern of land use around the village, the zones would be perfectly circular. Figure 3.27 shows that they are not. Can you suggest reasons for this?

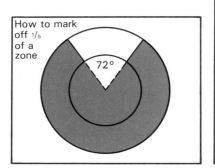

Fig. 3.30
How to mark off ⅕ of a zone

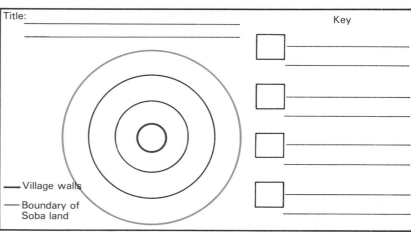

Fig. 3.31

Fig. 3.32
Cultivation in the savanna of West Africa
(a) Northern Ghana: a walled homestead and a crop of bullrush millet
(b) Southern Mali: grain storage bins with maize and sorghum being grown on poor soil

Exercise 3.14
Look at Figure 3.32.
(a) In what season were both the photographs taken? Explain your answer.
(b) In which photograph is cultivation most intensive?
(c) What reasons could explain the contrast between the quality of the crops?

Summary

In semi-arid areas, both animals and plants must adapt to the problem of drought for much of the year. Similarly, when man lives in such an environment, he must adapt his farming methods. As far as traditional ways of life are concerned, man may follow the example of the wild herbivores and move his herds between pastures or grow a restricted range of crops which can withstand drought. Methods such as bush fallowing may be used so as to conserve soil quality. However, as population pressure increases in an area, pastures may be overgrazed and cultivation may become permanent.

4 Man in tropical highlands

Mountain areas are looked on by man in quite different ways in contrasting parts of the world. Sometimes this may reflect the relief and climate of the mountain areas. For example, an area of steep slopes with a cold, wet climate in an otherwise temperate area such as Europe will be unsuitable for almost all types of agriculture, whereas an area of less steep slopes with a warm climate in a tropical area may attract farming settlement on a large scale. However, even within similar areas, people of different interests, occupations and cultures view mountain areas in different ways.

Exercise 4.1
Figure 4.1 shows evidence of some different ways in which man makes use of highland areas. The types of use shown are:
1. forestry,
2. a hydro-electric power scheme,
3. extensive livestock farming,
4. a tourist resort,
5. intensive cultivation,
6. mining.
(a) Fit each description to the correct picture, arranging the information in a table as in Figure 4.2.
(b) Decide whether each use of highland areas is most likely to be found in a temperate area, in a tropical area, or could be found in both. Indicate your decision by entering ticks in the 2nd and 3rd columns of your copy of the table.
(c) Where you have put a tick in only one of the columns, give reasons why you think the activities concerned are likely to be found only in temperate areas or only in tropical areas.

(e)

(f)

Fig. 4.1
How man makes use of the world's highlands

Picture	Uses of highland areas	Where found		Reasons
		Temperate area	Tropical area	
A B C D E F				

Fig. 4.2
Man in highland areas

42

The importance to man of highlands in tropical areas can be seen clearly when relief maps and population distribution maps of countries with large areas of highlands are compared. Figure 4.3 shows such maps for three countries.

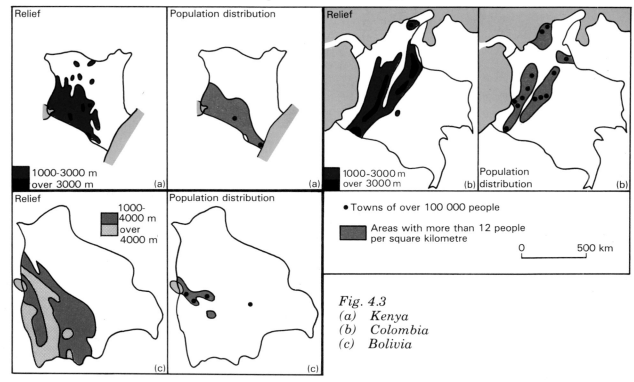

Fig. 4.3
(a) Kenya
(b) Colombia
(c) Bolivia

Exercise 4.2
(a) Do the densely populated areas correlate with all of the highland areas in the three countries? If not, what part of the highland areas do they avoid? Suggest reasons for your answer.
(b) In the two countries with coastlines there are some areas of dense settlement with important towns near the coast. What are the likely reasons for this?

In South America the importance of highland areas for settlement stretches far back into the past. The Andes Mountains were the centre of the Inca civilisation (Figure 4.4). The Incas grew a large variety of crops, practised irrigation, terraced hillsides, built cities and linked their settlements together by a military road running through the mountains. When the Spanish conquered South America they were attracted to the highland areas by their mineral wealth, in the case of the central Andes, or by climatic conditions which were more attractive to live and farm in than the low-lying, hot, disease-ridden forested lowlands in Colombia. Similarly, when British rule was established in Kenya, the high plateau was particularly attractive to farmers from temperate countries.

In Chapter 1 we saw in the photograph of Mount Kilimanjaro (Figure 1.4) that with increasing height, temperatures become lower. We also noted that many mountain areas have a higher rainfall than the surrounding lowlands. Figure 4.5 shows how vegetation zones in Colombia, South America, are related to height above sea level,

Fig. 4.4
The Inca city of Machu Picchu, Peru

reflecting the lower temperatures at greater heights. Notice that the lowest zone is rain forest associated with an equatorial climate.

Farming will clearly be impossible in the highest zones of Colombia because of very low temperatures, but there are areas above 2500 m on which some farming takes place. Because of the variety of temperature conditions to be found in Colombia, a very wide range of crops can be grown. They range from those of the tropical rain forest to those which normally grow in cool temperate conditions (for example, from cocoa to potatoes).

Figure 4.6 shows the altitudes at which the major crops grown in Colombia are found. You will notice that in the higher, cooler areas crops familiar to us in temperate areas are grown. However, one important point must be borne in mind. The areas which grown temperate crops such as wheat or potatoes, while cool for tropical latitudes, will not experience seasons or a variation in the length of day between one part of the year and another, as in temperate latitudes. As a result, temperate tree crops such as apples, which are geared to the changing seasons for flowering and fruiting, do not grow successfully. (Can you imagine what happens?)

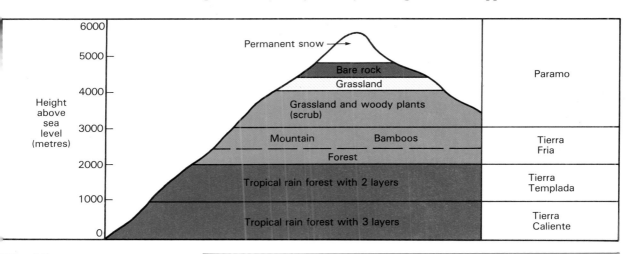

Fig. 4.5
Vegetation zones in Colombia

Exercise 4.3
Figure 4.7 shows a simplified contour map of a highland area based on part of Colombia.
(a) By referring to Figure 4.5, on a copy of the map use different shadings to show the extents of:
(i) the Tierra Caliente (tropical rain forest with 3 layers),
(ii) the Tierra Templada (tropical rain forest with 2 layers),
(iii) the Tierra Fria (mountain forest with moss and bamboos),
(iv) the Paramo (scrub and grassland),
(v) areas of bare rock and permanent snow.
Add a key to explain the various shadings.

(b) Several contrasting types of farming are found in this area:
(i) coffee plantations,
(ii) peasant farms growing potatoes and wheat,
(iii) peasant farms growing maize, rice and beans with cocoa as a cash crop,
(iv) peasant farms growing maize, plantains and beans with coffee as a cash crop,
(v) sugar cane plantations also growing rice.

44

Letters A to E on the map indicate the locations of these types of farm. Decide which locations are appropriate for the five types of farm and record the information in your key to the map. (Refer to Figure 4.6 and also bear in mind that nearness to transport is most important for plantations producing crops for export).

Fig. 4.6
The distribution of crops with altitude in Colombia

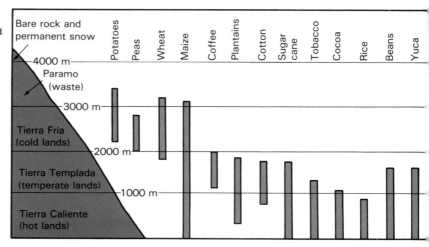

Fig. 4.7
A tropical highland area

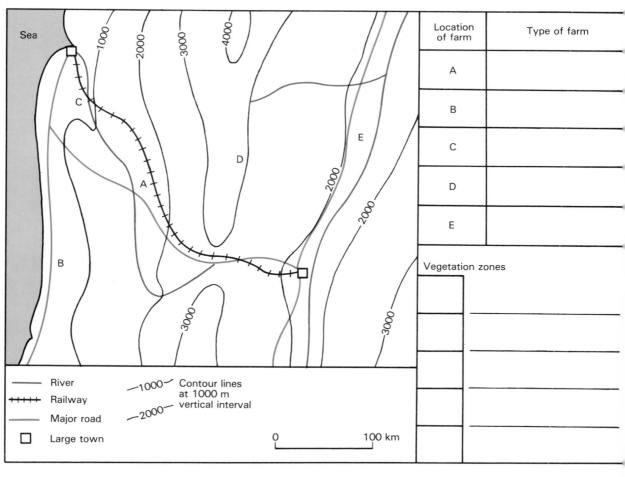

Location of farm	Type of farm
A	
B	
C	
D	
E	

Vegetation zones

River
Railway
Major road
Large town

—1000— Contour lines at 1000 m
—2000— vertical interval

0   100 km

Land-use patterns in a valley

If the land farmed by an individual farmer ranges over different heights, as in a valley, then we may expect him to produce a variety of crops normally grown in a variety of climatic zones. We might also expect land-use zones to be more closely related to physical factors than to distance from a settlement. Figure 4.8 is a map of a valley in the Bamenda Highlands in Cameroon, West Africa. The lower, less steep slopes of the valley have been farmed for hundreds of years. However, more recently cultivated land has been extended further up the valley sides and on to steeper slopes, owing to increasing population and the wish to produce a cash crop (coffee). Now, little forest is left and farming is advancing onto the grazing land used by Fulani cattle herders. (What problems may be caused by these new developments?)

Fig. 4.8
Land use in a valley in the Bamenda Highlands, Cameroon

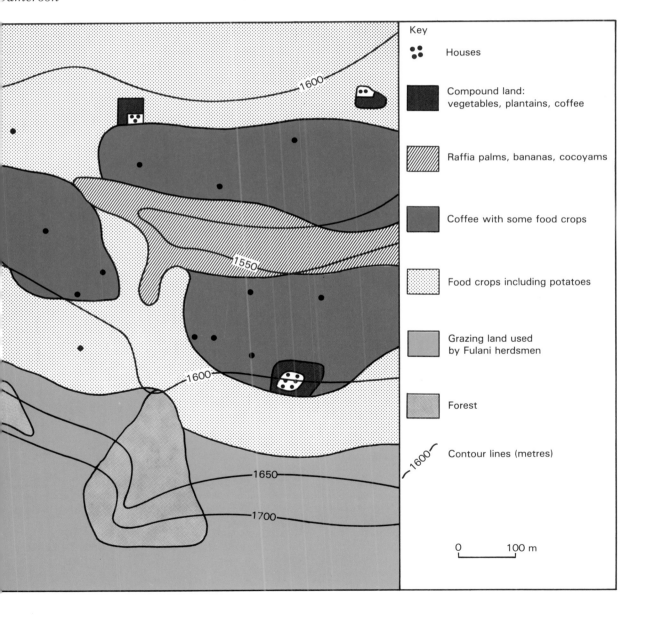

46

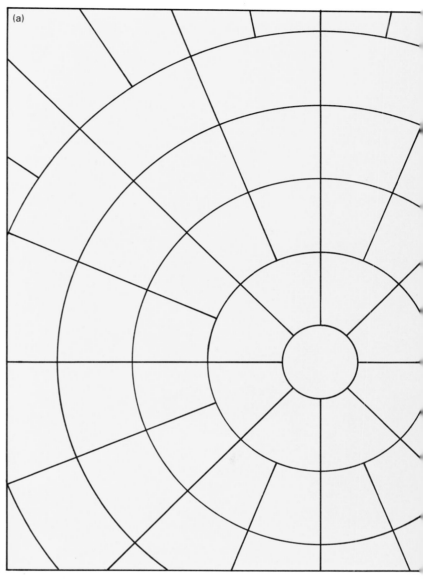

(a)

Fig. 4.9(a)

Exercise 4.4

(a)   On a piece of tracing paper draw Grid (a) (Figure 4.9(a)). Put it over the map of the valley and in each space indicate the most important land use. Then shade in the spaces, using different colours for the various land uses. Note that the grid is centred on the main village.

(b)   Does a clear pattern of circular land-use zones stand out as with the village of Soba in Chapter 3? If not, do the distributions of just one or two land uses show a relationship with distance from the village? Explain any relationship which may exist.

(c)   On a second piece of tracing paper, draw Grid (b) (Figure 4.9(b)). Put it over the map. Notice that it uses the contour lines to show zones of different altitude. Again, in each space indicate the most important land use, using the same colours as before. Fix both of your maps in your book and add a key.

(d)   Describe the pattern shown on your second map. Mention the relief of the land where forest still exists.

(e)   Three contrasting crops grown in the valley are bananas, coffee and potatoes. In what climatic zones would you normally expect to find these crops?

(f)   What conclusions can you draw about the influence on land use in this valley in the Bamenda Highlands?

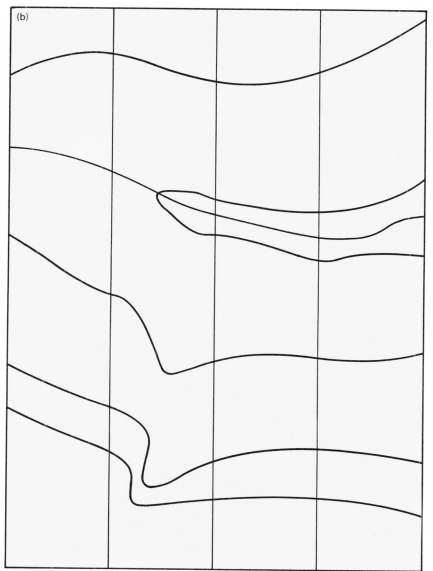

Fig. 4.9(b)

Different ways of farming in the highlands

Land in the same highland area can be used quite differently by different people. Figure 4.10 gives details of two contrasting farms in the highlands of Kenya, East Africa. In Chapter 2, we saw that a convenient way of comparing farms was by looking at them as systems. Figure 4.11 shows a systems diagram for the large commercial farm. Notice how complex it is compared with the systems diagrams of the farms in Chapter 2 (Figure 2.16).

48

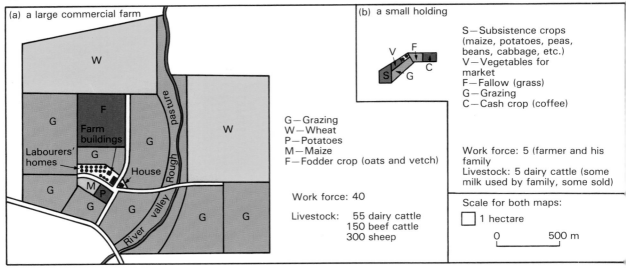

Fig. 4.10
Farms in the highlands of Kenya

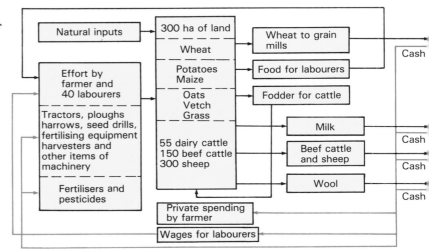

Fig. 4.11
A large commercial farm, Kenya

Exercise 4.5
(a) The systems diagram for the peasant smallholding will be very similar in layout to that of the farm in eastern Nigeria in Figure 2.16. The main difference is that the Kenyan farm has livestock. Draw a systems diagram for the Kenyan peasant smallholding, using information from Figure 4.10.
(b) Compare your diagram with the one in Figure 4.11 of the large commercial farm.
(i) Which farm has the greatest input by machinery and other modern methods?
(ii) Which farm has the strongest links with outside systems such as markets and transport?

Another way in which we can compare the farms is by seeing how intensively the land is used. We already know that intensive farming means that much labour is put into a small area in order to obtain a large amount of produce from it. A convenient method of measuring this is therefore to divide the area of the farm by the number of people working on it.

Fig. 4.12 (above-left)
Traditional farming methods in
East Africa
Fig. 4.13 (above-right)
Harvesting oats and vetch for
fodder on a large commercial
farm in Kenya

Exercise 4.6
Calculate the area per man (units: ha /man) for each farm. Which farm is the most intensive?

We must bear in mind, however, that this method of looking at the intensity of farming does not take into account how *efficiently* labour is used. Figures 4.12 and 4.13 show the contrast between work on a peasant farm and on a large farm in East Africa.

Exercise 4.7
Explain how labour is being used more efficiently on the large Kenyan farm than on the peasant farm. Why would it be difficult for the peasant farmer to make rapid changes in his methods?

Changes in farming the highlands

Kenya became an independent country in 1963. Until then, a large part of the Highlands was under European-owned farms and estates. Since independence, many of these farms have been divided up among African farmers. The Kenyan peasant farm we have studied used to be part of a European farm. Other large farms are now managed by Kenyans while some are still run by Europeans.

Exercise 4.8
Suggest why the Kenyan government did not split up all the European farms immediately when the country became independent. Suggest why some are still worked as large units. (Consider both farming methods and the importance of crops for export to Kenya.)

The Kenyan Highlands: tourism and settlement

Figure 4.14 shows part of the Kenyan tourist map of the Aberdare mountains in the Kenyan Highlands. This area is famous for its wildlife and scenery. The government has encouraged the tourist

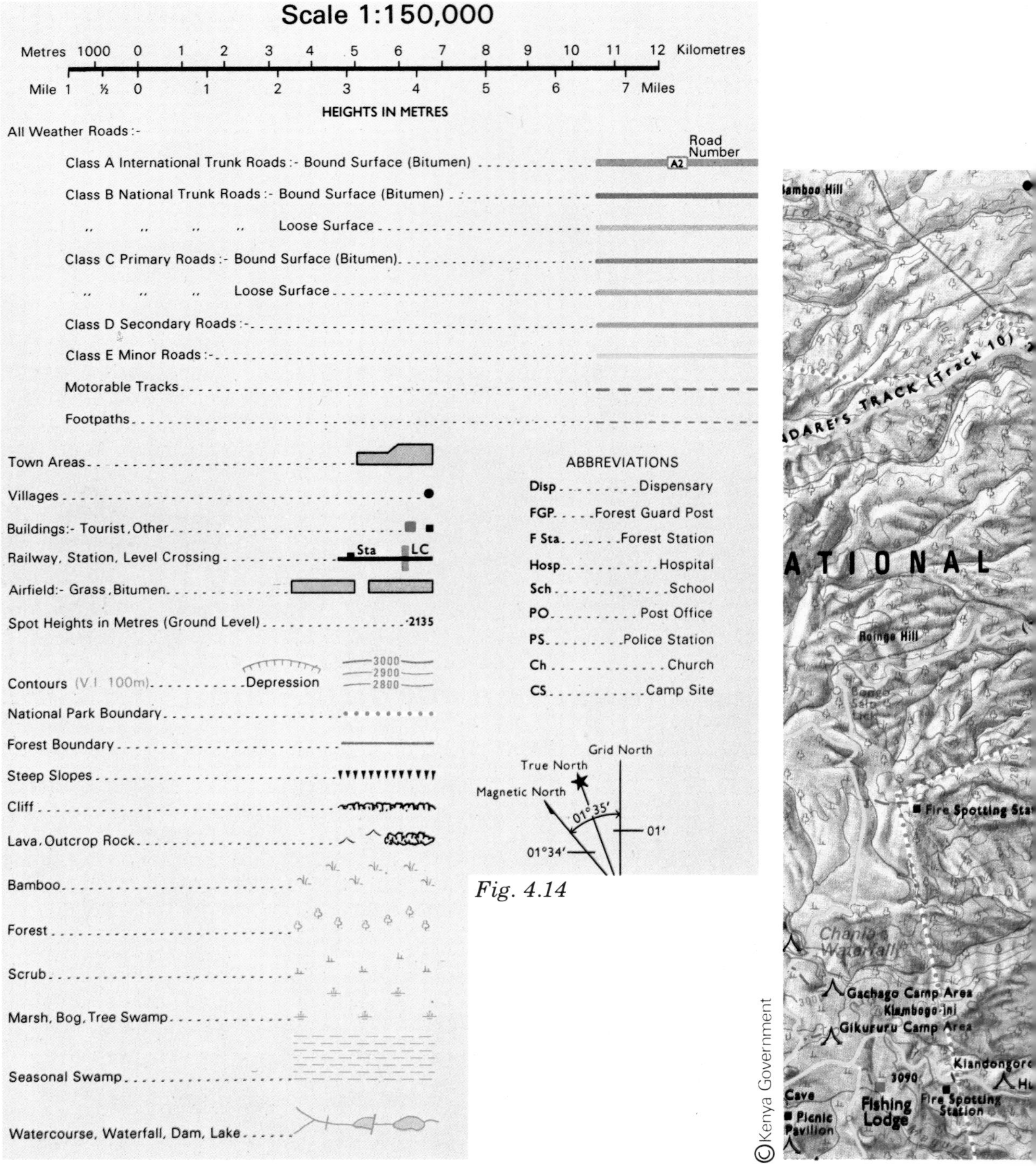
Scale 1:150,000
Metres 1000 0 1 2 3 4 5 6 7 8 9 10 11 12 Kilometres
Mile 1 ½ 0 1 2 3 4 5 6 7 Miles
HEIGHTS IN METRES
All Weather Roads :-
Road Number
Class A International Trunk Roads :- Bound Surface (Bitumen)
A2
Class B National Trunk Roads :- Bound Surface (Bitumen)
" " " " Loose Surface
Class C Primary Roads :- Bound Surface (Bitumen)
" " " Loose Surface
Class D Secondary Roads :-
Class E Minor Roads :-
Motorable Tracks
Footpaths
Town Areas
Villages
Buildings:- Tourist, Other
Railway, Station, Level Crossing
Sta
LC
Airfield:- Grass, Bitumen
Spot Heights in Metres (Ground Level)
·2135
Contours (V.I. 100m)
Depression
3000
2900
2800
National Park Boundary
Forest Boundary
Steep Slopes
Cliff
Lava, Outcrop Rock
Bamboo
Forest
Scrub
Marsh, Bog, Tree Swamp
Seasonal Swamp
Watercourse, Waterfall, Dam, Lake
ABBREVIATIONS
Disp.........Dispensary
FGP.....Forest Guard Post
F Sta.......Forest Station
Hosp...........Hospital
Sch.............School
PO...........Post Office
PS.........Police Station
Ch..............Church
CS...........Camp Site
Grid North
True North
Magnetic North
01°35′
01′
01°34′
Bamboo Hill
DARE'S TRACK (Track 10)
ATIONAL
Roinge Hill
Fire Spotting Sta
Chania Waterfall
Gachago Camp Area
Kiambogo-ini
Gikururu Camp Area
Kiandongoro
Cave
Picnic Pavilion
3090
Fishing Lodge
Fire Spotting Station
©Kenya Government

Fig. 4.14

ndustry as the visitors bring in much-needed money to Kenya. So as
o look after the wildlife and their environment much of the area has
een made into the Aberdares National Park. Outside the national
park there are villages and farms similar to the smallholding in
Figure 4.10.

Fig. 4.15
Treetops

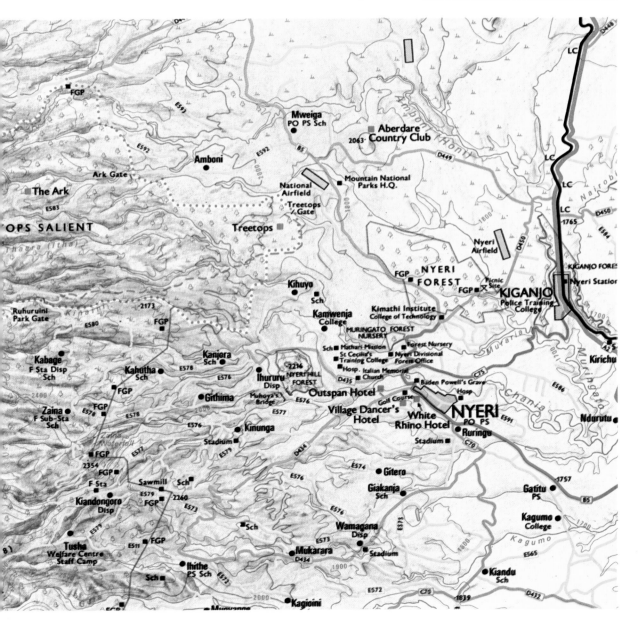

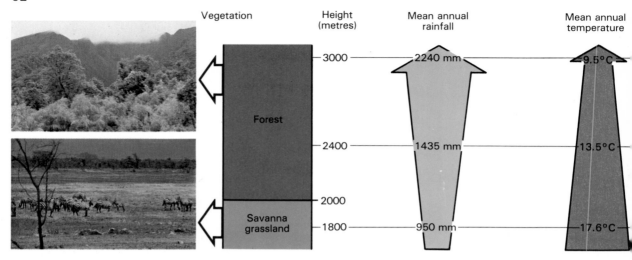

Fig. 4.16
The relationship between height, climate and vegetation in the Kenyan Highlands

Exercise 4.9

(a)   What is the highest point shown on the map and what is the lowest? In what parts of the map are these two points?

(b)   Most of the lower land is grassland. What is the main type of vegetation on the higher ground?

(c)   Inside the National Park there are places called 'Treetops' and 'The Ark'. What are these places?

(d)   What other places marked on the map may be of interest to tourists?

(e)   Many of the roads are very twisty with many hairpin bends. Why is this? What will the surface of most roads be like?

(f)   At the edge of the forest are buildings with the letters FGP by them. What is an FGP? Suggest why they are needed.

(g)   Figure 4.16 shows how annual rainfall totals, temperature and vegetation are related to height in this area. If you look at the map, you will notice that most of the villages (and therefore farms) are on the lower slopes of the mountains. What problems would farmers be faced with if they farmed:

(i)   the lower ground (below 1800 m),

(ii)   the higher slopes of the mountains (above 2400 m)?

(h)   Marked on the map there are several different types of building which provide services for people living in the area.

(i)   What services are found in some of the villages?

(ii)   What services are found in or near the towns of Nyeri and Kiganjo?

Why would these services be found in the towns rather than in the villages?

Summary

Kenya is an example of a tropical country with its population concentrated into the highlands. In fact, in several tropical countries with large areas of highland, such areas form the *economic heartland* of those countries. The main reason for this is usually the wide variety of crops that can be grown, often under more favourable conditions for settlement than in the lowlands, which are usually either hot and densely forested or semi-arid. Other factors such as the existence of minerals may attract people to the highlands. However, in many of these countries, population pressure in the highlands and the wish of the governments to develop lowlands for export crops has led to people moving out of the highland areas.

5 Export crops

Britain and other industrial countries of Europe cannot produce all the food they require. So, they must import from other countries. Some of these foods can be, and are, produced in Europe but additional amounts are imported from other temperate countries. Wheat, dairy products, meat and some fruits are examples. Others cannot be produced in Europe as they are tropical or sub-tropical crops. The developing countries of tropical areas are therefore possible sources of supply. Figure 5.1 shows a range of foods and drinks, the raw materials for which are produced in tropical areas. Tropical areas also supply raw materials for industry from their crops; rubber is the most important example.

On the other hand, the developing countries require many of the manufactured goods made in the developed countries. To buy these, they must sell their crops and minerals. This exchange of goods between developing and developed countries may seem straightforward and fair. However, the demand for trade first came from the European countries, who from the 16th century onwards established colonies in tropical areas in order to secure supplies of tropical crops. Plantations were established, until the 19th century often using slave labour. In the 20th century, European and North American companies have still had the controlling hand in trade between the developing and developed countries. Many of the tropical products are processed and packed in Europe and North America rather than in the developing countries.

> **Exercise 5.1**
> List the products shown in Figure 5.1. At the side of your list write down
> (i)   what processing or packing is needed to get the crop into the form shown in the photograph,
> (ii) whether most of the processing or packing is likely to be carried on in the exporting country or the importing country.

In recent years, the developing countries have begun to have a larger say in world trade. Many countries which were once ruled from Europe have become independent. Countries which are exporters of a particular product have got together so as to be in a stronger bargain-

Fig. 5.1

ing position with the industrial countries. The oil-producing countries formed OPEC (the Organisation of Petroleum Exporting Countries) and have demanded, and got, high prices for their oil. The export crop producers have also formed some organisations so that they can bargain together with the richer countries, but they have usually been less successful than OPEC. Some countries have taken over the export crop plantations of foreign companies, while others have made sure that they have had an increased share of profits or take part in the running of companies' plantations.

In recent years, the prices of manufactured goods required by the developing countries have risen rapidly while the prices of many export crops have not risen so fast. As a result more export crops must be sold to pay for the same amount of manufactured goods. For example, in 1960 the export of 4.2 tonnes of rubber could earn enough to buy a tractor; in 1975, 12.5 tonnes of rubber were needed.

Exercise 5.2
(a) Show the figures in the example given above by means of a pictorial graph (for example, a bale of rubber could represent 1 tonne).
(b) Explain why these figures represent a problem for developing countries.

Raising the prices of export crops may not solve the problem for the developing countries. Higher prices may cause demand to fall. For some crops, such as rubber, man-made substitutes might be used increasingly if prices are raised too much.

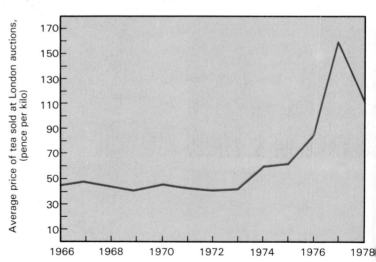

Fig. 5.2
The changing price of tea

Where a developing country has been able to obtain higher prices, one problem is that the increasing amounts of money coming into the country may pass to the few people who are already quite prosperous, rather than to the country's people generally. Let us have a look at the example of tea. In 1976 the average price of a ¼ lb packet of tea was 12 p but by 1977 it had risen to 30 p. This increase reflected the prices which were obtained for tea at the London auctions where the tea packing firms buy tea from the tea growers. Figure 5.2 shows tea auction prices since 1966; notice the rapid increases in 1975 and 1976. Who benefits from the rise in prices? The figures in Figure 5.4 help to provide an answer to this question.

Fig. 5.3 (above-left)
Picking tea on an estate in India
Fig. 5.4 (above-right)
Tea: from India to England

Exercise 5.3
(a)   Plot the figures given in Figure 5.4 on graphs using the axes given in Figure 5.5.
(b)   Look at your completed graphs. Do the tea workers appear to have done as well as might be expected from the price increases?

Although the developing countries wish to have greater control over the trade in their exports, they still require the money and technical knowledge of the richer countries in order to develop their resources. The large companies may build houses, roads, schools and hospitals, which will help the people in the areas they work.

Plantations

The cash crops mentioned in earlier chapters are export crops. They were grown either on small farms or on plantations. When grown on a small farm in developing countries, the cash crop usually occupies only a small part of the farmer's land; most of the land is used for subsistence crops. We looked at examples of such farms in Chapters 2, 3 and 4. Plantations cover large areas and employ large numbers of people. For example, the American rubber company Firestone owns two particularly large plantations in Liberia, West Africa, which together employ 25 000 people and are covered by 11 500 000 rubber trees. Many plantations are owned by large companies who manufacture the goods made from the plantation crops. Examples include the major tyre companies, Unilever (whose products include margarine and soaps made from palm oil) and Brooke Bond Liebig. Other plantations, usually smaller ones, are owned by smaller companies not involved in manufacturing, or by the governments of developing countries; these plantations may grow a variety of crops for export. Let us now have a closer look at the growth of export crop production in developing countries.

Figure 5.6 is a map of an imaginary tropical region, Zageria. In the following exercise we will see how export crop production may develop over time in this region.

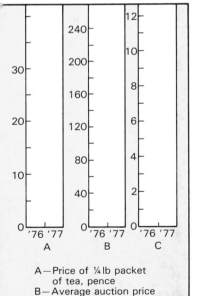

A—Price of ¼ lb packet
   of tea, pence
B—Average auction price
   of tea, pence per kilo
C—Basic wage of tea
   worker in India,
   rupees per day

Fig. 5.5
Tea statistics, 1976–7

56

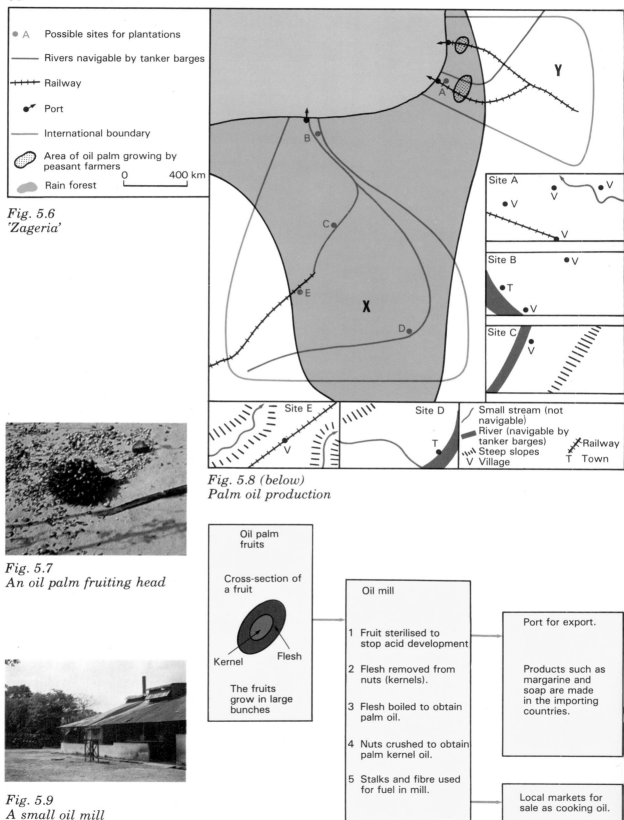

Fig. 5.6
'Zageria'

Fig. 5.7
An oil palm fruiting head

Fig. 5.8 (below)
Palm oil production

Fig. 5.9
A small oil mill

	Chosen sites	Reasons
1890	1. 2.	
1950	1. 2.	

Fig. 5.10
Choices of location for palm oil production

Exercise 5.4   Choosing locations for palm oil production

The class needs to be divided into groups of five, each group to represent the Board of Directors of a company manufacturing a wide variety of products including margarine and soap. Palm oil is the main raw material required. (Figure 5.8 shows how the oil is obtained.) Besides their other responsibilities, the directors will be involved in finding and developing sources of palm oil for their company's factories. The directors are:

The Transport Manager, whose main concern is getting the palm oil from the producing location to the port and then to the factories as cheaply and smoothly as possible.

The Personnel Manager, who is responsible for seeing that a labour force can be obtained to work on any plantation that may be established.

The Plantation Planning Manager, who is responsible for making sure that possible locations for plantations are well-suited to growing oil palms, and for laying out the plantation. He is also keen to maintain high standards of palm quality.

The Financial Director, who wishes to spend as little money as possible in developing sources of supply and wishes to make as large a profit as possible.

The Chairman, who supervises discussion and aims to make decisions in the light of all available information.

Each member of the class should have a copy of Figure 5.10 in which to record the decisions made during the exercise, together with reasons for them.

Stage 1: 1890
The company has decided to invest a large amount of money into developing oil palm plantations in Zageria. The company's surveyors have selected five possible sites (A to E on Figure 5.6) and the directors must choose two of them. They must consider the information shown on the map and bear in mind the following points:

(a)   The European power which rules country X is keen to develop its colony and will sell land 10 times more cheaply than the power which rules country Y.

(b)   The most economical method of transporting palm oil is by tanker barge on rivers. The only other possible method over long distances is by railway.

(c)   The plantations' oil extracting factory must be close to a navigable river. Plenty of water is needed for the factory.

(d)   Flat land at a site enables roads for transporting the fruit to the factory to be laid out easily.

(e)   If an area has a low population density, workers must be brought in from other areas and housing built for them. If an area is densely populated, workers can stay in their villages, but if very densely populated, there may be little room to expand the plantation in future. In many densely populated areas farmers may well be growing oil palm themselves.

Each director will, of course, wish to make a choice from his own point of view. Once a group has discussed the possible sites, each director must vote for two sites. The two sites with the most votes will be used for the plantations. If the number of votes for a particular site are equal, the chairman will have the casting vote.

The chosen sites should be entered in the table together with reasons for their choice.

Stage 2: 1950
The company has expanded its manufacture of margarine and soap, and needs to double its supply of palm oil. The present Board of Directors meets to decide how to obtain the additional oil. The following points must be considered:

(a)   Two new sites for plantations could be chosen. However, another possibility is to choose one new plantation site and to obtain the rest of the oil by buying it from peasant farmers in country Y. This will mean that less money needs to be spent straightaway. The growing of oil palms would not, of course, be in the hands of the company.

(b)   Land in country X is now only a little cheaper than in country Y.

(c)   The other points to consider are the same as points (b), (c), (d) and (e) in 1890.

Look at Figure 5.6, which shows the possible plantation sites and the location of oil palm growing by peasant farmers. The directors should each vote for two choices which, together with reasons, should be entered in the table.

58

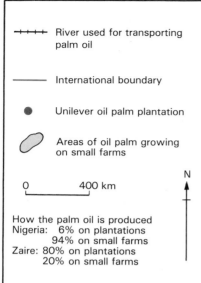

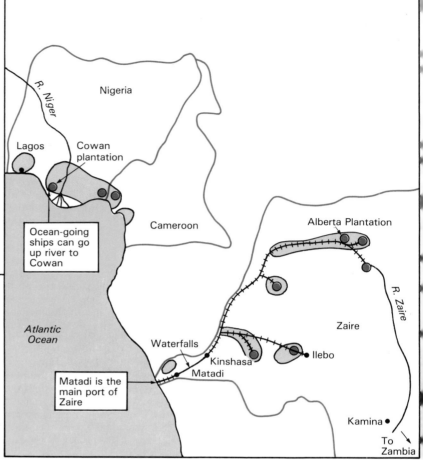

Fig. 5.11
Palm-oil production in part of Africa

Palm oil from Nigeria and Zaire

Fig. 5.12
A rubber plantation in Malaysia.

Figure 5.11 is a map of part of Africa, including the large countries of Nigeria and Zaire. If you turn the maps used for the oil palm game sideways, you will notice that the imaginary region of Zageria is closely based on this part of Africa. On Figure 5.11 the oil palm plantations belonging to the Unilever Company have been marked together with areas of palm oil production from small farms. In the corner of the map, figures for Nigeria and Zaire show how their palm oil production is divided between plantations and small farms.

Exercise 5.5
(a) Make a copy of that part of Figure 5.11 which shows Zaire. On your map mark in Zaire's railways as follows:
(i) from Kinshasa to Matadi,
(ii) from Ilebo to Kamina and off the southern edge of the map.
   Mark in with arrows the likely export routes for the palm oil to the ports by river and/or rail from each of the plantations.
(b) By your map draw two bars 10 cm long and then subdivide them to represent the division of palm oil production between plantations and small farms in Nigeria and in Zaire (1 cm will represent 10%). Label the bars clearly.

Fig. 5.13
Inside a rubber factory in Malaysia

Fig. 5.14
Rubber-producing areas in Brazil, Liberia and Malaysia
(a)   Brazil
(b)   Liberia
(c)   Malaysia

(c)   In which country will the export of palm oil be easiest? To explain your answer, describe the route taken by palm oil from:
(i)   Cowan in Nigeria,
(ii)   Alberta in Zaire.
(d)   Look at a population distribution map of Africa in an atlas. Considering point (e) in the 1890 stage of Exercise 5.4, explain the pattern shown by your divided bar graphs of how palm oil is produced in Nigeria and Zaire.

Whether export crop production develops on plantations or small farms depends on many other factors besides population density in an area, of course. Most plantations in Africa and south-east Asia were developed when the countries of these regions were colonies of European countries. Sometimes, the ruling country would find the native farmers well-organised and would buy crops directly from them rather than set up plantations. This was so with oil palm production in Nigeria.

Rubber plantations

In looking at oil-palm production, we saw that good transport links and a plentiful supply of labour were necessary for the successful development of plantations producing export crops. A look at the production of rubber will show the same influences at work together with some other factors. Figure 5.12 shows a view of a rubber plantation in Malaysia, south-east Asia. Until recently, almost all rubber was grown on plantations rather than small farms because:

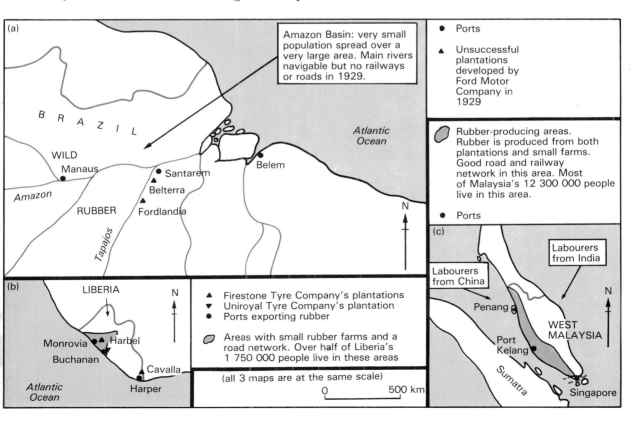

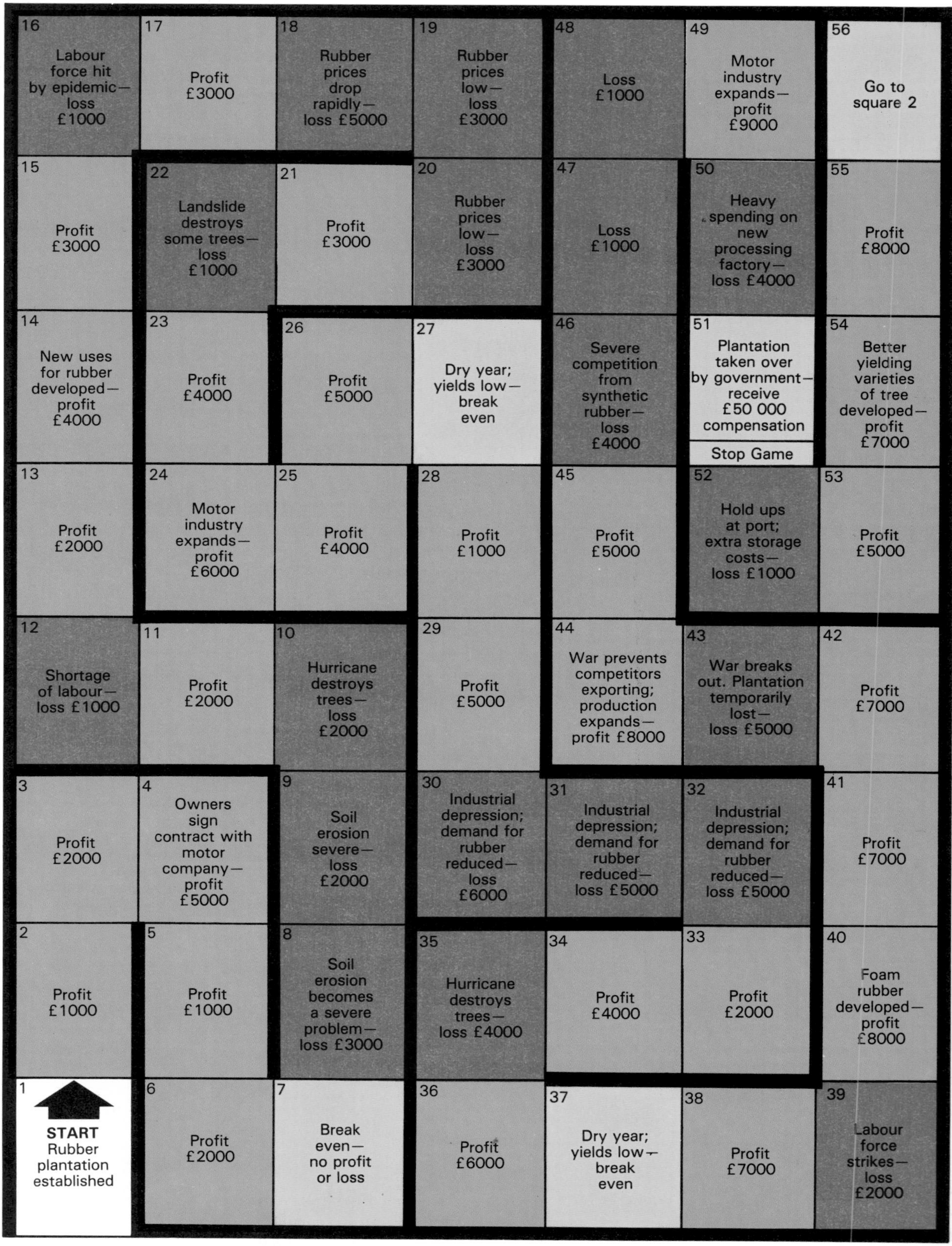

16 Labour force hit by epidemic— loss £1000

17 Profit £3000

18 Rubber prices drop rapidly— loss £5000

19 Rubber prices low— loss £3000

48 Loss £1000

49 Motor industry expands— profit £9000

56 Go to square 2

15 Profit £3000

22 Landslide destroys some trees— loss £1000

21 Profit £3000

20 Rubber prices low— loss £3000

47 Loss £1000

50 Heavy spending on new processing factory— loss £4000

55 Profit £8000

14 New uses for rubber developed— profit £4000

23 Profit £4000

26 Profit £5000

27 Dry year; yields low— break even

46 Severe competition from synthetic rubber— loss £4000

51 Plantation taken over by government— receive £50 000 compensation
Stop Game

54 Better yielding varieties of tree developed— profit £7000

13 Profit £2000

24 Motor industry expands— profit £6000

25 Profit £4000

28 Profit £1000

45 Profit £5000

52 Hold ups at port; extra storage costs— loss £1000

53 Profit £5000

12 Shortage of labour— loss £1000

11 Profit £2000

10 Hurricane destroys trees— loss £2000

29 Profit £5000

44 War prevents competitors exporting; production expands— profit £8000

43 War breaks out. Plantation temporarily lost— loss £5000

42 Profit £7000

3 Profit £2000

4 Owners sign contract with motor company— profit £5000

9 Soil erosion severe— loss £2000

30 Industrial depression; demand for rubber reduced— loss £6000

31 Industrial depression; demand for rubber reduced— loss £5000

32 Industrial depression; demand for rubber reduced— loss £5000

41 Profit £7000

2 Profit £1000

5 Profit £1000

8 Soil erosion becomes a severe problem— loss £3000

35 Hurricane destroys trees— loss £4000

34 Profit £4000

33 Profit £2000

40 Foam rubber developed— profit £8000

1 ↑ START Rubber plantation established

6 Profit £2000

7 Break even— no profit or loss

36 Profit £6000

37 Dry year; yields low— break even

38 Profit £7000

39 Labour force strikes— loss £2000

Fig. 5.15 The rubber plantation game

1.   Trees are not ready for production until they are six years old. Individual farmers usually cannot afford to wait this time before they get money coming in.

2.   A factory is needed to turn the latex (the fluid which comes out of a cut made in the trunk of the tree) into liquid rubber or solid raw rubber (Figure 5.13).

3.   It was easier to train workers in growing rubber tree seedlings and tapping the trees for latex on a plantation than to deal with many small farmers.

Figure 5.14 shows maps of three rubber-producing countries in different continents: Brazil, Liberia and Malaysia. The rubber tree is native to the rain forests of Brazil and until the beginning of the 20th century, all the world's rubber came from wild rubber trees in the Amazon Basin of Brazil. The town of Manaus became the centre of a rubber 'boom' and large fortunes were made. To keep prices high, Brazil forbade the export of rubber seeds but in 1876 seeds were smuggled out to Kew Gardens in London. The seedlings produced were taken to Malaysia (then the British colony of Malaya) in order to establish rubber plantations on which rubber could be produced far more cheaply than from the wild trees in Brazil. The Ford Motor Company tried to develop rubber plantations in 1929 at Fordlandia and at Belterra in Brazil (Figure 5.14) but the schemes failed.

Exercise 5.6
(a)   Considering the nature of tropical rain forests, why do you think rubber could be produced more cheaply on plantations than from wild rubber trees in Brazil?
(b)   Look at Figure 5.14. From evidence on the maps suggest why rubber plantations in Malaysia and Liberia were successful but Ford's plantations in Brazil failed. (Consider transport and labour supply.)

The influences at work on rubber production are shown in Figure 5.15, which is in the form of a board game. As can be seen from Ford's failures, the correct choice of location will influence how successful a plantation is, but there are many other influences.

Exercise 5.7
Play the rubber plantation board game. The rules are as follows:
1.   Before starting to play, make a copy of Figure 5.16, which is an accounts table on which you will record the profits and losses that you make.
2.   A move following the throw of the dice represents one year.
3.   When you land on a square, note the profit or loss that you make and enter it in your accounts table. Notice that a column is provided to keep a running total of your profits (or losses). For example, if in Year 1 a profit of £2000 was made and in Year 2, £3000, the running total entry for Year 2 would be £5000.
4.   On squares where losses occur or profits are very large, reasons are given. When you land on such squares, write down the reasons in the last column of your accounts table.
5.   There is no finish shown on Figure 5.15. If you come to the last square (56) you return to Square 2 and continue until you have thrown the dice and moved a total of 20 times.

Year	Profit or loss	Running total	Reasons for losses or large profits
1			
2			
3			

Continue the table to Year 20.

Fig. 5.16
Accounts table for the rubber plantation game

When you come to the end of the game and compare your final profit with others, you will see that some have been far more successful than others. This has happened in reality; the events in the game are based on historical facts. For example, the first attempt to produce rubber in Liberia in 1910 failed because rubber prices had dropped to one-quarter of 1910 prices by 1915. Another reason for the failure of Ford's plantations in Brazil was the industrial depression of the 1930s, when demand for manufactured goods including cars and rubber products fell rapidly. Again, during the Second World War, Malaya was occupied by the Japanese and the supply of rubber to Europe was cut off. However, at the same time production in Liberia was expanded to make up for this lost source of supply.

Exercise 5.8
Write an account of (a) the factors which encourage the successful development of rubber production, and (b) the factors which will hinder the development of rubber production. You will need to refer both to the rubber plantation game and to the previous paragraph.

Ports and transport for export crops

If you look back at Figure 5.14 you will see that rubber production is limited to certain areas of Liberia and Malaysia. Let us have a look at the reasons for this in the case of Malaysia. All of the country has climatic conditions suitable for rubber production. Figure 5.17 shows the distribution of rubber-producing areas in West Malaysia. Environmental factors other than climate, namely relief and soils, may give some clue to this distribution. Figure 5.18 shows the distribution of the mountain areas, where steep slopes have thin soils and make laying out plantations difficult. Clearly these environmental factors are important, because rubber production avoids mountain areas. However, there are large areas of suitable land where rubber production is not found.

The existence of a good transport network to the ports which export the crop is essential for successful export crop production. Figure 5.18 also shows West Malaysia's railway network and the location of the ports. Notice that the larger rubber-producing areas are near the railways and ports. The railway running along the west side of the country has had a very marked effect on the distribution of rubber growing. This is because it already existed when rubber was introduced to the area. Many plantations were established near the railway between 1895 and 1925. The railway running across the centre of the country to Tumpat on the east coast was not finished until 1931. By that time, rubber production was no longer expanding and so few plantations were established near this line.

Exercise 5.9
Draw a map of West Malaysia marking the rubber-growing areas, the main towns and the railways. At the end of an arrow pointing to the western part of the country, list reasons for the importance of rubber production here. At the end of a second arrow pointing to the eastern and central part of West Malaysia, list reasons why rubber production is not important here.

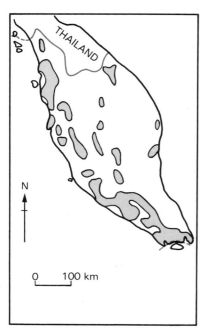

Fig. 5.17
Rubber-producing areas
in West Malaysia

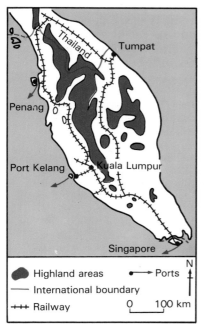

Fig. 5.18
West Malaysia: highland areas,
railways and ports

Export crops from small farms

In many developing countries, the production of export crops from small farms is increasing while production from plantations is becoming less important, or is remaining the same. This is true of rubber production in Malaysia and Liberia, although as we saw earlier there are problems in producing rubber on small farms. Figure 5.19 shows how the changes are taking place in different ways in the two countries.

Fig. 5.19
Increasing rubber production from small farms

Fig. 5.20
Rubber growing on small farms

Exercise 5.10
(a) At the beginning of the section on rubber plantations, several problems of growing rubber on small farms were mentioned. Look at Figure 5.19 and then say how the problems are being solved in
(i) Malaysia,
(ii) Liberia.
(b) In which country is the change doing least harm to the plantation owners? In which country is the change helping the small farmers the most? Explain your answers.

	Malaysia	Liberia
Transport	Roads already built to serve rubber plantations and tin mines used.	Roads already built by Firestone Rubber Co. between rubber plantations and ports used.
Helping farmers to make a start	Land already planted with rubber bought from rubber companies and handed over to landless families. Loans for buying equipment available from government.	Firestone supplies seeds and gives advice.
Processing the rubber in factories	Government provides money to set up factories, which serve a large number of farmers.	Firestone buys up all rubber production which goes to the plantation factories

Figure 5.21 is a map of a rubber-growing area in Malaysia. The area is near the coast and is flat and low-lying. As rubber trees require well-drained soils to grow well, drainage ditches have had to be dug. Most of the paths on the map follow the ditches. In the west of the area the rubber is grown on small farms, while in the east it is produced by plantations, named on the map.

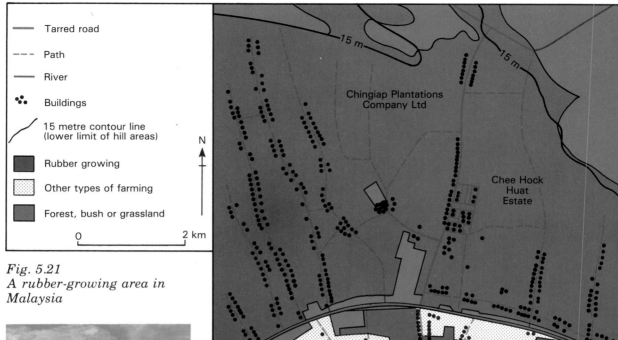

Tarred road

Path

River

Buildings

15 metre contour line
(lower limit of hill areas)

Rubber growing

Other types of farming

Forest, bush or grassland

0   2 km

N

Fig. 5.21
A rubber-growing area in
Malaysia

Chingiap Plantations
Company Ltd

Chee Hock
Huat
Estate

15 m

15 m

Fig. 5.22
Rubber growing on terraced
hillsides. Young rubber trees
(seedlings) have just been
planted

Exercise 5.11
(a) Look at Figure 5.21. Describe how the patterns of paths and the distribution of buildings in the area of small farms differs from those in the area where rubber is grown on plantations.
(b) In what areas of the map is rubber *not* grown?
(c) Figure 5.22 shows a newly cleared area where young rubber trees (seedlings) are being planted.
(i) How does the relief of this area differ from the area shown on the map?
(ii) What work has had to be done on the land before the planting of the seedlings? Why would this work be necessary?

Summary

Export crops are vital to the well-being of many developing countries. Money earned from their sale to other countries is needed to obtain goods and materials that developing countries do not produce and to provide services such as medical care and education. The export crops are also important to the developed countries, who usually started their production in the first place. Because of this, the developed countries have usually had the greatest say in trade between the two groups of countries. One way the developing countries can increase the benefit they get from export crops is by processing them before they are exported, so that a more valuable product can be sold abroad.

In the past, plantations established by the developed countries were the usual way of producing export crops. Plantations are still very important indeed, but many developing countries are encouraging individual farmers to grow export crops alongside their subsistence crops. Whatever the method of farming used, good transport links to ports are very important for the successful production of export crops. Because transport networks in developing countries are usually poor, export-crop production is often restricted to small areas.

6 Export minerals

Production of Copper Ore (Million Tonnes of Copper Content), 1977	
USA	1377
USSR	1140
Chile	1056
Canada	785
Zambia	658
Zaire	498
Peru	320
Philippines	274
Poland	268
Australia	221

Consumption of Copper (Million Tonnes), 1977	
USA	2000
USSR	1250
Japan	1131
West Germany	742
United Kingdom	512
France	378
China	350
Italy	315
Belgium	295
Canada	219

Developing countries in

Fig. 6.1
World production and consumption of copper

Although the developing countries of the world account for only a small proportion of the world's production of manufactured goods, they account for a much larger proportion of the world's production of raw materials. These are needed by factories to make the manufactured goods. Timber and some of the export crops mentioned in the previous chapter are raw materials for some industries. More important for industry are mineral resources, in particular, metals. Because the major manufacturing countries in North America and Europe, together with Japan, cannot produce all the minerals they need, they look to the developing countries. Figure 6.1 shows the *production* figures for the world's ten leading producers of copper ore. It also lists the *consumption* figures of copper for the ten leading users of copper.

Exercise 6.1
(a) Make a list of some important uses of copper.
(b) Draw bar graphs
(i) to compare copper-ore productions of the ten leading producers,
(ii) to compare copper consumption of the ten leading users.
Use vertical scales of 1 cm to 200 million tonnes. Shade in the bars of the developing countries in a contrasting colour to those of the developed countries.
(c) Describe the patterns shown on the two sets of graphs. What is the main conclusion that can be drawn from them?

Accessibility

When the industrial countries look to the developing countries for minerals, their aim will be to obtain those minerals at the lowest cost to themselves. The costs involved in the transport of minerals are an important part of total costs to the user. In a developing country, it is possible that there will be no railway nor even a road near a mineral deposit. Therefore, to obtain the mineral a railway may have to be built, a very costly exercise. The *accessibility* of the mineral deposit is therefore important and will often be the deciding factor as to whether mining will take place or not.

Exercise 6.2
Study the map of West Africa (Figure 6.2), which shows the location of mining centres. Minerals have to be sent to the coast for export. It classifies the mining centres according to their importance: major, secondary or minor.
(a) Using the axes drawn in Figure 6.3, draw a graph to show the relationship between the distribution of mining centres and their distance from the coast, as follows:
    A major centre counts 3 points.
    A secondary centre counts 2 points.
    A minor centre counts 1 point.
Total the points 'scored' for each distance zone shown on the map and plot the score on the graph. (If a centre lies on the line between two zones, include it in the zone nearest the coast.) For example, if a zone had 2 major, 3 secondary and 1 minor centres,

66

it would score (2 × 3) plus (3 × 2) plus (1 × 1) points or 13 points.
(b)   Write a description of the relationship shown between the importance of mining and distance from the coast.

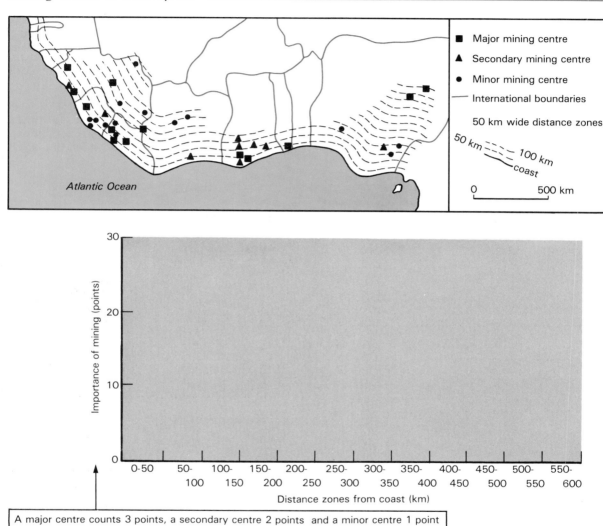

Fig. 6.2
Mining centres in West Africa

A major centre counts 3 points, a secondary centre 2 points and a minor centre 1 point

Fig. 6.3
The relationship between the distribution of mining centres and their distance from the coast

Ore grades and prices

The accessibility of a mineral deposit is not the only thing which decides whether it will be mined or not. The *reserves* (the total quantity of the mineral in a deposit) must be large enough to be worth mining. Two other factors are *the grade of the ore* and *the possible selling price of the mineral*. We need to have a closer look at these two factors to see exactly what they mean.

Metals do not occur in a pure state in large amounts. They are mixed up with other minerals in rock. Rocks which contain metallic minerals worth mining are known as *ores*. It is often not worth mining low quality ores because it will be more expensive to mine and transport the ore and to get the metal out of the ore in the smelting

---

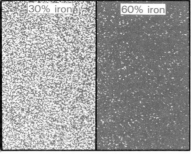

works. For example, twice as much rock with a 30% iron content must be mined and transported as with a 60% iron content (Figure 6.4).

This brings us to the other factor—the selling price of the mineral. As you probably know, if something is in short supply, its price usually goes up. This has happened with many minerals. They may be in short *supply* because *demand* has increased. An increase in the price of a mineral may mean that it will be worth mining a low-grade ore despite the extra mining costs, or a less accessible deposit despite the extra transport costs. Exercise 6.3 shows how these factors work.

Fig. 6.4 Grades of iron ore *Fig. 6.5 (below) Mining iron ore in 'Zarebia'*

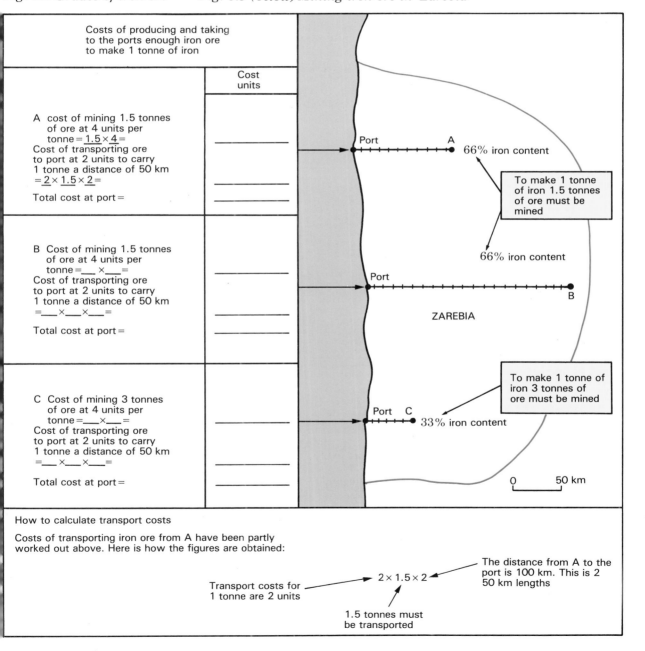

Fig. 6.6
Iron ore

Exercise 6.3

Study Figure 6.5, which is a map of Zarebia, an imaginary developing country with important reserves of iron ore. Reserves in amounts worth mining exist at points A, B and C. You will notice that the locations are at different distances from the coast. Two deposits have a 66% iron content, one a 33% iron content. The cost of mining one tonne of iron ore is 4 units. The expected transport costs, which of course partly reflect the cost of building the railways, are 2 units to carry one tonne a distance of 50 km.

(a)   On a copy of Figure 6.5, calculate the costs of producing and taking to the ports enough iron ore to make one tonne of ore. For location A the figures you need to use have already been entered on Figure 6.5. The figures for the transport of ore have been obtained as shown at the bottom of Figure 6.5. The total cost of the ore at the port for each location is simply obtained by adding the cost of mining to the cost of transport.

(b)   If the selling price of iron ore is 15 units per tonne, which deposit would it pay to mine? Why would it not pay to mine the other two?

(c)   Suppose that in the future the selling price of iron ore rose to 20 units per tonne. Explain why it would now pay to mine the less accessible deposit and the poorer quality one.

Fig. 6.7
Liberia: iron-ore mining

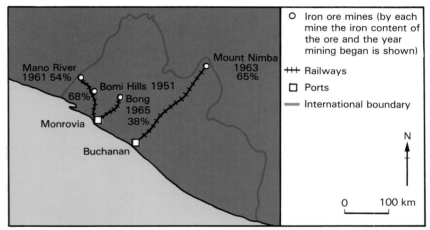

Fig. 6.8
Mount Nimba iron-ore mine, Liberia

Fig. 6.9
Loading a truck with iron ore at Mount Nimba

Exercise 6.4

Figure 6.7 is a map showing Liberia in West Africa and its iron-ore mining centres. At each centre the quality of the ore and the date mining began are shown. Under the heading 'Iron-Ore Mining in Liberia' answer the following questions. (You will need to compare the pattern in Liberia with imaginary Zarebia in Exercise 6.3).

(a)   Suggest why the Bomi Hills iron ore was mined first.

(b)   Suggest why mining of the (i) the Bong iron ore and (ii) the Mount Nimba iron ore began after the mining of the other two deposits.

Transport routes for minerals

The building of transport links between mines and export ports is one of the main expenses of developing a mineral resource. Construction materials have to be imported, skilled workers and engineers may not be available locally and the terrain across which the railway has to be built may be difficult. Also, it is often necessary to build a port at the seaward end of a line in order to load the mineral on to the ships. Minerals are often the main starting point of a railway network in a developing country and may help the country's development in other ways, such as encouraging the production of export crops.

The exercises below look at some export routes in two contrasting African countries; Mauritania in West Africa, and Swaziland in the south-east of the continent. Mauritania is a large country (more than four times as big as the United Kingdom), yet has a population of under 1 million people. Almost all of the country is desert. A rich deposit of iron ore has been developed at F'Derik (Figure 6.10).

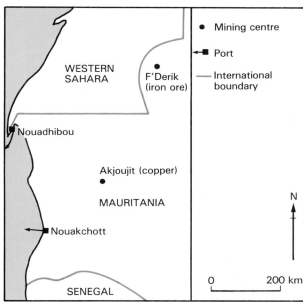

Fig. 6.10 (above-left)
The iron-ore mine at F'Derik, Mauritania

Fig. 6.11 (above-right)
Mining centres and ports in Mauritania

Exercise 6.5

(a) Trace the map of Mauritania (Figure 6.11). On your map mark in the shortest route over which a railway line could be built from F'Derik to the nearest port, without crossing the international boundary.

(b) Calculate the detour index of the route from F'Derik to the port. (How to calculate a detour index is explained in Chapter 2.) Write the index by the route.

(c) In 1968 it was decided to develop a deposit of copper at Akjoujit. Mark in the shortest route over which a railway line or road could be built from Akjoujit to the nearest port. Calculate its detour index and write it in by the route.

The detour made by the F'Derik railway line is an example of a *negative deviation*; the route deliberately avoided passing through another country. A negative deviation is also made when difficult land lies on the straight route, making it cheaper to build a longer railway around the difficult part.

Swaziland is a small country of half a million people in which farming is important, unlike Mauritania. In 1964 a railway was opened between the iron-ore mines at Bomvu Ridge (Figure 6.12) and

70

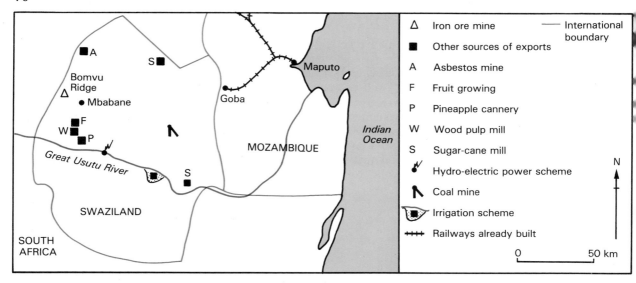

Fig. 6.12
Swaziland

an existing railway at Goba in Mozambique which leads to the port of Maputo. As well as making small negative deviations to avoid hills, the railway was diverted from a straight line in order to pass through areas where it could attract other trade and help to develop export crops. Such a detour is an example of a *positive deviation*.

Fig. 6.13
Export routes of copper from Zambia

Exercise 6.6
(a)   On a copy of the map of Swaziland, mark on a route for the railway from Bomvu Ridge to Goba which you think would be of use to farming as well. It may not pay to build the line through *every* area producing crops if it means that very large deviations are necessary. Road links to the railway could be used instead. Also, bear in mind the fact that as Swaziland has reserves of coal, it was decided to haul trains by steam locomotives at first.
(b)   Calculate the detour index for your route and enter it on the map.
(c)   Suggest why the builders of the railways in Mauritania did not make a positive deviation similar to that made in Swaziland.

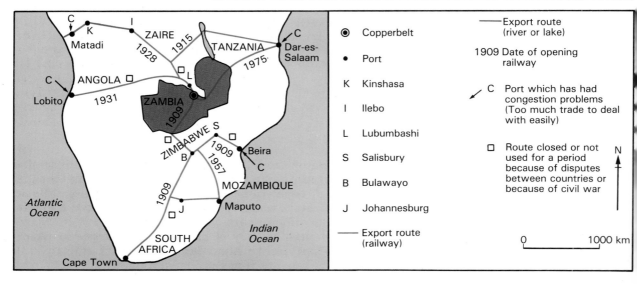

Export routes for land-locked countries

Swaziland is a land-locked state and has to use a port in a neighbouring country to export its products. For land-locked states in the centre of continents, this can be a very severe problem.

The country which has had the most difficulty in developing export routes is Zambia in Central Africa. Zambia is the fifth largest producer of copper in the world and its economy depends very heavily on copper exports. Figure 6.13 shows the large number of different routes which have been used for exporting copper. One reason for so many routes being used is that as new railways were built they proved to be shorter or more suitable than routes already in use. Other reasons are shown on Figure 6.13.

Exercise 6.7
(a) Take the export route Copperbelt–Lubumbashi–Ilebo–Kinshasa–Matadi. Using an atlas map of southern Africa, trace this route, marking clearly the sections of the route which are by rail and the section by water transport. Mark on and name the largest towns. Label the points where changes in transport must be made, '*transhipment points*'. Also, by referring to Figure 6.13, label other problems which have been met with in the use of this route.
(b) Make a list of the problems which have affected the export routes used by Zambian copper.

Problems in developing mineral resources

Transport is not the only problem involved in developing mineral deposits in the Third World. Labour is needed to work in the mines, on the railways and at the ports. A developing country may not have the skilled technicians and engineers which are needed; as a result, it will have to look to developed countries. The developed countries have to be looked to for money as well. Railways, mines and ports have to be built before the mines produce any metal ore for sale. To obtain the *capital* for development, a country may have to sell the right to develop the mineral to the highest bidder, a company from another country which wants to pay as little as possible for the mineral. Even when development is by the producing country itself, money has to be borrowed from abroad.

Let us see how these problems were dealt with in the case of developing Mauritania's iron ore. The area had a very small population; construction labourers came from neighbouring Senegal besides other parts of Mauritania. Housing had to be built for the workers at the mine and at the port. Mauritania had little money itself to develop the iron ore. A company called MIFERMA was set up to develop the ore with money coming from Britain, France, West Germany and Italy. These countries are the main users of iron ore from Mauritania.

Fig. 6.14
A conveyor belt taking iron ore from the mine to the railway at F'Derik, Mauritania

How minerals occur and are mined

The appearance of an area where mining is taking place varies greatly between one location and another. The main reason for this is the nature of the mineral deposit. Figure 6.15 shows three ways in which minerals commonly occur:
1.   in lodes or veins,
2.   in huge masses in igneous rocks, and
3.   in river gravels.

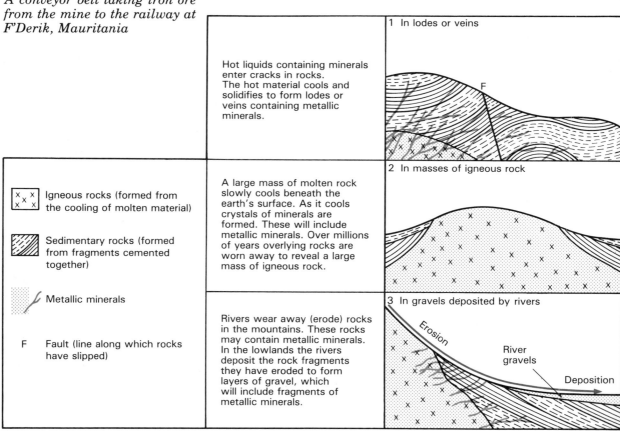

Fig. 6.15
How minerals occur

Figure 6.16 shows four mining methods: underground, open-cast, gravel pumping, gravel dredging. Sometimes, more than one of these methods is used in an area. At first, deposits near the surface may be mined by open-cast methods and then shafts will be sunk to mine deeper deposits.

73

(b)

(d)

Fig. 6.16
Mining methods:
(a) Underground mining
(b) Open-cast mining
(c) Gravel pumping in a Malaysia tin mine. High pressure jets of water wash the gravel containing tin into these sluices, where the heavy tin is separated out
(d) Gravel dredging for tin in Malaysia. The dredger scoops up the gravel containing tin. The tin is removed from the gravel inside the dredger and the waste is dumped back into the water

Fig. 6.17
Stages in the production of copper

Producing metals from ores

When pure metal is made from an ore the process is called *smelting*. Many mineral ores are not smelted in the countries where they are mined, but in the developed countries. However, if smelting takes place in a producing country then it will obtain larger profits. Also, smelting works will provide work in the country and may attract other industries. Before many ores are sent to the smelting works, they are crushed and as much of the waste rock as possible is separated out. This is known as *concentrating*. The flow diagram in Figure 6.17 shows the stages in producing copper. Copper is often obtained from very lean ores. The ore in the diagram contains 5% copper, a typical figure. Ninety-five per cent of the rock which is mined is therefore waste.

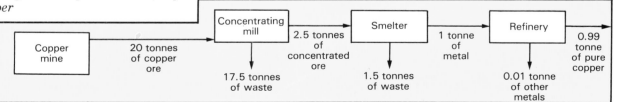

Copper concentrating, smelting and refining
Copper wire and cables
Food products
Soft drinks and beer
Shoes
Textiles
Furniture
Chemicals
Cement
Tobacco
Printing
Metal goods
Clothing

Fig. 6.18 (above-left)
A Copperbelt mining landscape. In the right background is an open-cast mine, in the centre a concentrating mill and in the right foreground miners' housing

Fig. 6.19 (above-right)
Manufacturing industries in the Copperbelt, Zambia

Exercise 6.10

(a)   Put the heading 'Producing Metals for Ores' and suggest reasons for the following:
(i)   Copper concentrating mills are always built near the mines.
(ii)   Most, but not all, copper smelters are built in mining areas or at the exporting ports.
(iii)   Copper refineries are often built in the countries which make articles from copper.
(b)   In the steel industry, the iron and steel works take the place of the smelter and refinery. When iron ore is as high quality as that of Mauritania (63% iron content) why is a concentrating plant often not built?
(c)   Draw a flow diagram for aluminium production similar to the one for copper. (5 tonnes of aluminium ore (bauxite) are needed to produce 2 tonnes of concentrate (alumina) which will produce 1 tonne of aluminium. No refinery is necessary.)

We have seen that Zambia is one of the world's important producers of copper. It accounts for over 90% of the country's exports. We have also seen that copper-concentrating mills and usually copper smelters are located in mining areas. This is so in Zambia, as it is particularly important to save the cost of transporting waste over the very long export routes.

Most of Zambia's copper is also refined in the country, unlike that of several other important producers. The area where copper is mined in Zambia is known as the Copperbelt. As a result of copper mining and smelting, this area has become the main centre of population in Zambia. 20% of Zambia's 5 million people live here. Other industries have also grown up; some of the more important ones are listed in Figure 6.19. The other towns of importance in Zambia lie along the railway built to the Copperbelt from Rhodesia. Although Zambia remains a poor country, copper has provided her with much wealth to date.

Exercise 6.11

Look at Figure 6.19.
(a)   Which of the following phrases best describes most of the types of industry listed in the table:
   heavy industry; consumer goods; advanced technology goods?
(b)   Why would many of these industries grow up in the Copperbelt rather than in other parts of Zambia?

Iron ore and iron and steel making

Iron ore is the most important metal ore mined and we might therefore expect it to be the basis of industrial development. Yet most developing countries with deposits of iron do not have iron and steel works. This is partly because the deposits were developed by foreign iron and steel companies for their own needs. There are other reasons for this, though. Figure 6.20 provides some clues. It lists those developing countries which produce important amounts of iron ore. For each country, the following information is given:

1. iron-ore production,
2. steel production (if any),
3. total population,
4. average yearly income per person.

Country	Iron ore production 1975 (million tonnes)	Steel production 1975 (million tonnes)	Population (millions)	Average yearly income per person (£)
Brazil	46.6	8.3	109.2	503
China	32.5	29.0	852.1	111
India	26.0	7.9	610.1	76
Liberia	17.0	—	1.8	131
Venezuela	15.4	1.1	12.4	1131
Chile	6.8	0.5	10.5	368
Mauritania	5.6	—	1.3	102
Peru	5.1	0.4	16.1	288
North Korea	3.8	2.8	16.3	211
Mexico	3.4	5.2	62.3	378
Angola	3.4	—	5.8	283
Algeria	1.7	0.2	17.3	367
Swaziland	1.4	—	0.5	212
Turkey	1.3	1.5	40.2	307
Sierra Leone	0.9	—	3.1	128

Fig. 6.20
Developing countries which are important producers of iron ore

Exercise 6.12

(a) On a copy of Figure 6.21 rank the countries according to their populations. Write in their steel-production figures and underline those countries which produce more than 1 million tonnes of steel a year.

(b) Again on the table, rank the countries according to their average income per person, which is an obvious way of measuring the prosperity of a country. Write in their steel-production figures and underline those countries which produce more than 1 million tonnes of steel a year.

(c) Look at the completed table. What factors appear to be necessary if a developing country producing iron ore is to have an iron and steel industry? Which factor appears to be the most important, if any? Attempt to explain your answers.

(d) Liberia plans to build an iron and steel works. What problems is she likely to face?

(e) Liberia's planned works would be built on the coast at Buchanan rather than at the iron-ore mines (see Figure 6.7). Suggest reasons for this, considering the facts that Liberia has no coal and much of the steel would have to be sold to other countries.

Mauritania		Ivory Coast	
Iron ore	93%	Coffee	32%
Others	7%	Timber	28%
		Cocoa	20%
		Others	20%

Liberia		Zambia	
Iron ore	75%	Copper	93%
Rubber	17%	Others	7%
Others	8%		

Nigeria

Oil	80%
Vegetable oils and seeds	7%
Cocoa	6%
Others	7%

Ghana		Zaire	
Cocoa	66%	Copper	60%
Timber	15%	Palm oil	7%
Aluminium	5%	Coffee	6%
Diamonds	5%	Diamonds	5%
Others	9%	Cobalt	5%
		Others	17%

Gabon

Oil	57%
Timber	21%
Manganese ore	19%
Others	3%

Tanzania

Cotton	16%
Coffee	15%
Diamonds	14%
Sisal	13%
Oil products	9%
Cashew nuts	6%
Others	27%

Kenya

Coffee	29%
Tea	14%
Oil products	14%
Pyrethrum	5%
Meat	5%
Others	33%

	Developing countries which produce iron ore, ranked according to population		Developing countries which produce iron ore, ranked according to income per person	
Rank	Country	Steel production (million tonnes)	Country	Steel production (million tonnes)
1				
2				
3				
4				

Fig. 6.21 (above) Steel-making in developing countries

The danger of depending on a single export

Many countries in the Third World have their exports dominated by either one mineral or one crop. Figure 6.22 shows the export trade of several African countries, most of which have been mentioned in this and the previous chapters.

Fig. 6.22 (left) The export trades of some African countries. (Products are named only when they account for at least 5% of the country's exports.)

Exercise 6.13

(a) Classify the countries in Figure 6.22 into three columns headed:
(i) Countries dominated by one export product (one product accounts for over 50% of exports).
(ii) Countries dominated by two export products (two products account for between 25% and 50% of exports each).
(iii) Countries with no dominant exports.
(b) Using the percentage figures in the table, draw pie graphs to show the export trade of one country from each of the columns. (In drawing the graphs remember that 1% will be represented by 3.6°.)
(c) What are the problems involved if a country's exports are dominated by one product? What might the country attempt to do in order to solve this problem?

Summary

Export minerals, like export crops, are vital to the economies of developing countries. These countries produce a very large part of man's mineral needs. Not all the reserves of minerals have been tapped. Whether mining takes place or not will depend firstly on the accessibility of mineral deposits but also on other factors such as the grade of the ore and on the selling price. Mining is an expensive operation and money may have to be obtained from other countries in order to build railways and ports besides the mines themselves. The new transport links may help to encourage the production of export crops while the minerals may be a foundation for industrial development. Although exporting minerals can bring much-needed wealth to a developing country, there are dangers. In the past especially, much of the wealth went to the countries who provided the money for development. Dependence on one export mineral by a country involves risks, not only because of the chance of a fall in prices but also because the mineral will one day be worked out.

7 Ports

The development of ports has always been very important to tropical countries. This is because they rely on the export of crops and minerals for their prosperity. Also, as they develop they need to import manufactured goods and materials for constructing roads, railways, power plants and factories. Most of the trade of such countries is with North America, Europe and Japan, rather than between themselves; trade by overland routes is usually not possible. As a result, trade must be through sea ports.

Trading by sea in most tropical areas was first developed by Europeans who wished to obtain slaves, tropical crops or precious metals. In the cases of East Africa and Asia, trade was first developed by the Arabs or Chinese. At this stage, ports would often consist of no more than a fort at a river mouth.

The development of ports

Let us have a closer look at a particular area to see how ports have developed. West Africa shows a clear pattern of port development under difficult conditions, for many countries in this area have no natural harbours. Large sections of coastline consist of broad beaches pounded by heavy surf. Behind the beaches lie lagoons and mangrove swamps (Figure 7.1). The Portuguese were the first Europeans to come to this area, in the late 15th century, in search of slaves. Other Europeans followed and established forts along the coast. The forts were served by boats which paddled out through the surf to ships lying at anchor offshore. With the ending of the slave trade in the 19th century and the development of an export trade in crops and minerals, more complex ports had to develop. Figure 7.2 shows the stages of port development in Ghana, from surf ports to modern man-made harbours. The exercise below looks at this development in greater detail.

Fig. 7.1 (below) Surf pounding a West African beach. Behind the beach is a lagoon with mangrove swamps. The lagoon's water has broken through the beach, but the surf has quickly healed the gap

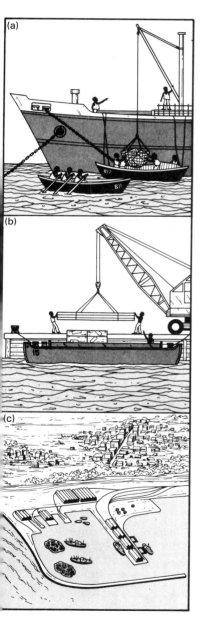

*Fig. 7.2
Port development in Ghana
(a) Surf boats
(b) Lighter unloading at a pier
(c) Takoradi, Ghana's first man-made harbour*

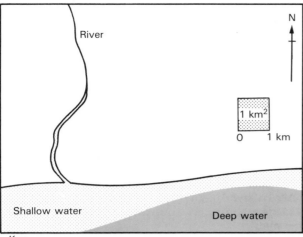

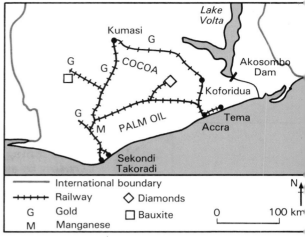

Key

	Fort built in 1600		Railway
	Town built by 1800		Town built between 1800 and 1900
	Location of surf boat beach and storage sheds of 1800		Breakwaters of deep-water harbour
	Small pier for lighters, 1900		Warehouse and factory area, 1970
	Warehouses, 1900		Housing built between 1900 and 1970

Fig. 7.3 (above-left)
The development of a port in
West Africa
Fig. 7.4 (above-right)
Southern Ghana

Exercise 7.1

Figure 7.3 shows a section of coastline typical of much of West Africa. It is broken by only one river, which is too shallow to be a suitable anchorage for ships.

Stage 1: 1600
European traders wish to obtain slaves from this area. An agreement is made with coastal tribes to capture slaves from tribes living inland. The only way to travel inland is by canoe. A fort is built on the coast to act as a base for slave trading. Surf boats are used to move slaves and cargo between the coast and ships anchored off shore. On a copy of the map, mark on the best location for a fort. Put the symbol you use in the key to the map.

Stage 2: 1800
Slaves remain the main item of trade. Other exports have been developed on a small scale. Because of increasing trade, a small town has grown up around the fort. On your map shade in an area of about 1 square kilometre to represent the town. Mark in the point at which surf boats would beach and storage sheds would be built. Add the shading and the symbol used to the key.

Stage 3: 1900
The slave trade has ended. Trade in goods such as palm oil, rubber, cocoa, timber and minerals has increased greatly. The following developments take place; add all of them to your map and to its key:

(i) A small pier is built for lighters (Figure 7.2), which can carry more cargo than surf boats can to the ships offshore. As existing storage sheds are still used, the pier must be close by them.
(ii) A new area of warehouses is built near the pier.
(iii) A railway is built from the port to the interior.
(iv) The town grows in size by about 2 square kilometres.

Stage 4: 1970
Exports have rapidly grown in importance. Lighters and surf boats cannot deal with the increasing amount. Also, imports of manufactured goods and construction materials have increased. It has been decided to build a large deep-water harbour in which ocean-going ships can berth. Mark on your map the new developments listed below. Add all symbols to your key.
(i) The deep-water harbour. It must be built on the coast at the point where the water is deepest offshore. The breakwaters which make up the harbour need to enclose an area of about 2 square kilometres.
(ii) Warehouses and factories are built on an area of about 1 square kilometre near the harbour.
(iii) A branch railway is built from the existing railway to the new harbour.
(iv) New housing covering an area of about 2 square kilometres is built near the new harbour.
(v) The older town continues to grow. Add to it an area of about 4 square kilometres.

Fig. 7.5
Accra from the air. The beach where surf boats used to draw up is next to the pier. Lighters and surf boats with larger items of cargo used to unload at the pier. Nearby can be seen warehouses once used for storing cargo and to their left an old fort. The tall buildings at the right are in Accra's central business district

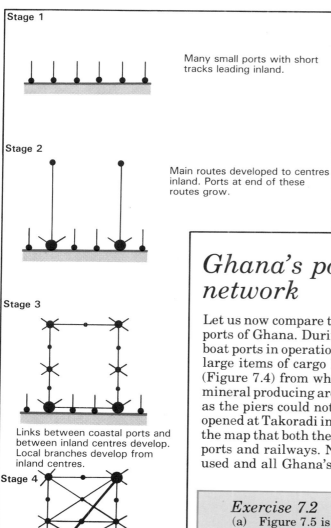

Stage 1

Many small ports with short tracks leading inland.

Stage 2

Main routes developed to centres inland. Ports at end of these routes grow.

Stage 3

Links between coastal ports and between inland centres develop. Local branches develop from inland centres.

Stage 4

Links develop between all centres. Busy main routes develop.

Fig. 7.6
Stages in the growth of a transport network in a developing country

Ghana's ports and transport network

Let us now compare the development of this imaginary port with the ports of Ghana. During the 19th century, Ghana had about 30 surf-boat ports in operation. By 1907 piers for lighters and surf boats with large items of cargo had been constructed at Accra and at Sekondi (Figure 7.4) from where railways were built to the export-crop and mineral producing areas inland. Surf-boat ports continued to be used, as the piers could not take all the trade. Deep-water harbours were opened at Takoradi in 1928 and at Tema in 1962. You will notice from the map that both these harbours were built near the existing lighter ports and railways. Now both surf boats and lighters are no longer used and all Ghana's trade passes through these two harbours.

Exercise 7.2
(a) Figure 7.5 is a view of Accra from the air. Place a piece of tracing paper over the photograph and trace the line of the coast. Shade in the sea. On your trace mark in and label a fort, the pier for lighters, old warehouses, the beach and the Central Business District.
(b) In the last century about 30 surf-boat ports were needed to deal with a very small amount of trade in Ghana. Now large quantities of cargo are handled by only two ports. Attempt to explain this *concentration* of trade.
(c) The deep-water harbours could not be built *at* Sekondi and Accra as the sites were unsuitable for building. However, they were built as near as possible to them. Why do you think this was done?

The development of ports in Ghana has taken place at the same time as the development of a transport network. The present-day railway network of the southern part of Ghana is shown on the map in Figure 7.4. Figure 7.6 shows four stages in the growth of a transport network in a developing country. Stage 1 shows a number of small ports with local tracks leading inland for a short distance. When Ghana had many surf boats dealing with a small amount of trade as in the 19th century, her transport network was at this stage. Stage 2 shows that routes penetrate inland and small settlements grow up at their end. Trade increases at the ports from which these routes lead. Stage 3 shows the development of routes between the coastal ports and between inland towns. Stage 4 shows the development of a complex pattern of routes between all the towns.

> ### Exercise 7.3
> (a) Consider Ghana's ports and railway network as they are today. Which stage would you think Ghana's network has now reached?
> (b) Redraw the diagram of the stage you believe Ghana is now at. On your diagram name Kumasi, Koforidua, Sekondi/Takoradi and Accra/Tema. Head your diagram 'Ghana's Ports and Railway Network Today'.

Fig. 7.7
The Akosombo Dam on the Volta River

Fig. 7.8
Tema

Three African ports: Tema, Mombasa and Buchanan

Tema

We have already seen that Tema is Ghana's new port, opened in 1962 to replace the inadequate surf-boat and lighter port at Accra, the capital of Ghana, 27 km to the west. The port was also developed in connection with the Volta Power Scheme. North of Tema the Volta River has been dammed by the Akosombo Dam to produce large amounts of hydro-electric power (Figure 7.7). Aluminium making needs a large supply of cheap electricity and a smelting works has been built at Tema. The new harbour is used to import alumina (concentrated aluminium ore) and to export aluminium. Other industries have also been developed at Tema including oil refining

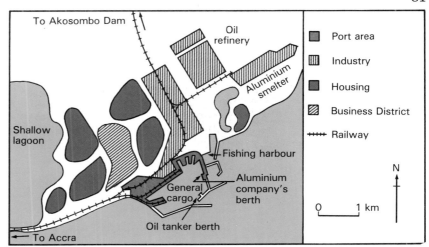

Fig. 7.9
The port of Tema, Ghana

concrete making and the manufacture of metal goods; many relying on imported raw materials. The layout of the new town and port is shown on the map in Figure 7.9. The new harbour itself consists of two large breakwaters enclosing general cargo berths, oil tanker berths, alumina berth, cocoa sheds and a ship repair dockyard. Tema handles about 2 million tonnes of cargo a year, exporting mainly cocoa, other tropical crops and aluminium, and importing mainly oil, construction materials and manufactured goods.

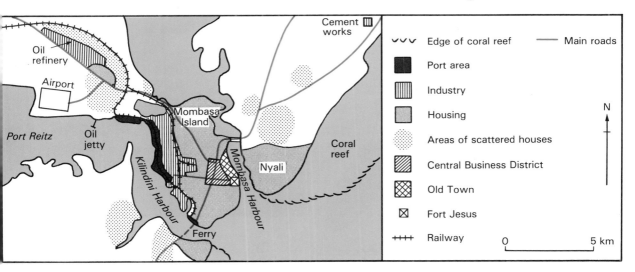

Fig. 7.10
The port of Mombasa, Kenya

Mombasa

Mombasa is the port of Kenya in East Africa. It also handles trade for Uganda and Tanzania. It first became a port 1000 years ago under the Arabs, who were attracted by its well-sheltered harbour and its defensive position on an island. Mombasa Harbour to the east of the island (see Figure 7.10) is now too shallow for modern ships, although it is still used by the Arab vessels known as dhows. The large ships use the deeper and wider Kilindini Harbour to the west of the island.

As at Tema, industries have grown up near the port. They include oil refining, steel rolling, metal goods, building materials, fish processing, fertilisers and ship repairing. Mombasa's exports include coffee, tea, sisal, cotton, meat, vegetable oils, copper and cement.

Fig. 7.11
The port of Mombasa

Imports are manufactured goods, construction materials and oil. Trade is rapidly increasing (5 760 000 tonnes in 1974) as it is at many ports in developing countries. This leads to problems of congestion, with ships having to wait for other ships to unload and clear the port. New berths for ships take time to construct and there may not be room for expansion. To speed up the handling of general cargo, a container berth has been built at Mombasa. If goods which are awkward to handle loose are packed inside containers (large weatherproof metal boxes of standard size) much time is saved.

Exercise 7.4

(a)   Look at the photographs of Mombasa in Figure 7.11. Which one is of Mombasa harbour and which one is of Kilindini Harbour? Give reasons for your answers and describe each photograph.
(b)(i)   Why is the old town of Mombasa located on the east side of the island?
(ii)   What are the natural advantages of Mombasa as a site for a modern port?
(iii)   Describe and explain the location of the industrial areas.
(iv)   What problems are there in having a large town like Mombasa sited on an island?
(v)   Where could new berths for large ships be built in the future?

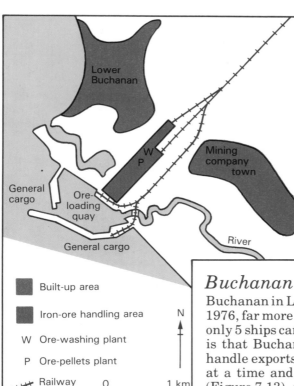

Fig. 7.12
The port of Buchanan,
Liberia

Fig. 7.13
An iron-ore carrier

Buchanan

Buchanan in Liberia handled no less than 9 330 000 tonnes of cargo in 1976, far more than Tema or Mombasa, yet the port town is small and only 5 ships can be handled at a time (Figure 7.12). The reason for this is that Buchanan is a specialised ore terminal, opened in 1963 to handle exports of iron ore. As each train brings in 8500 tonnes of ore at a time and the port handles bulk ore carriers of 70 000 tonnes (Figure 7.13), a very large total of cargo handled is built up. General cargo accounts for only about one-hundredth of the tonnage handled. Except for plants which wash iron ore and make it into pellets, no industrial development has taken place at Buchanan. There are plans to build an iron and steel works to supply Liberia and other West African countries.

Amount of cargo handled in a year	
Main exports	
Main imports	
Type of harbour (natural or manmade)	
Industries	
Problems	

Exercise 7.5
(a)   Summarise the features of these three African ports, under the headings given in Figure 7.14.
(b)   What are the main features that the ports of Tema and Mombasa have in common?
(c)   What is the main similarity between Tema and Buchanan?
(d)   Suggest why Tema and Mombasa have become important industrial centres but Buchanan has not.
(e)   If an iron and steel works was built at Buchanan, what do you think the main changes would be (i) at the port, (ii) in the town?

Fig. 7.14

Hinterlands

We saw that Mombasa exports goods which come from all over Kenya and from other countries. It imports goods for distribution by rail and road to the same area. This trading area is Mombasa's *hinterland*.

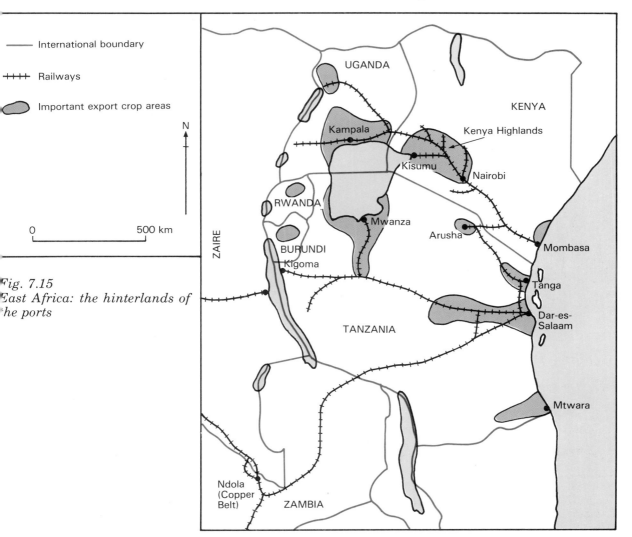

Fig. 7.15
East Africa: the hinterlands of the ports

Port	Trade (tonnes)
Mombasa	6 760 000
Tanga	280 000
Dar es Salaam	3 737 000
Mtwara	290 000

Fig. 7.16
Trade handled at East African ports (1974)

The quantity of a port's trade depends to a great extent on the size of its hinterland. In turn, the size of a port's hinterland depends on how good its transport links inland are. Let us have a look to see how this works in an actual region. The map in Figure 7.15 shows the location of Mombasa and other ports in East Africa. Figure 7.16 gives figures for the trade of each port.

Exercise 7.6
You will require as a base map an exact copy of the coastline, lakes and international boundaries on the map in Figure 7.15. Mark and name the four ports. On your map draw circles proportional to the tonnage handled for each port. Use a scale for the radius of each circle of 1 cm for every 1 000 000 tonnes of cargo. The centre of each circle will be the port it represents; leave out the part of each circle which goes into the sea. That part of each circle on land will represent the relative importance of each port.

The circles do not, however, represent the shape or the size of the ports' hinterlands very well. This is because (1) they take no notice of the transport links which lead to the ports; (2) some hinterlands may produce far more than others of the same size. For example, a hinterland containing a rich farming area producing export crops will give rise to more trade than one covering a sparsely populated desert region with few natural resources.

Exercise 7.7
Take a piece of tracing paper and place it over the map in Figure 7.15. Trace only the coastline, the lakes and the positions of the four ports. On the tracing paper draw the ports' hinterlands as follows:
(a) Mombasa's hinterland is Kenya, Uganda, Rwanda and the Arusha area of Tanzania.
(b) Tanga's hinterland is the area served by the railway running inland to Arusha. The Arusha area is therefore in the hinterland of two ports.
(c) Mtwara's hinterland is the southernmost part of Tanzania.
(d) Dar-es-Salaam's hinterland includes Tanzania (except for the areas in the hinterlands of Tanga and Mtwara), Burundi and northern Zambia, including the Copperbelt.
Fix your tracing paper over the map drawn for Exercise 7.6.

Exercise 7.8
(a) Suggest why the hinterland of Tanga is smaller than the hinterland of both Mombasa and Dar-es-Salaam. Suggest why the hinterland trade of Mtwara is small.
(b) Why is the Arusha area in the hinterlands of both Mombasa and Tanga?
(c) Figure 7.16 shows that Mombasa's trade is greater than that of Dar-es-Salaam. Yet Dar-es-Salaam has a larger hinterland than Mombasa. Attempt to explain this.
(d) Zambia has only recently become part of the hinterland of Dar-es-Salaam. Look back at Figure 6.13 and then explain this development.

Singapore, a world port

Some ports have developed beyond being an outlet for a country's export crops or minerals and an entry point for imported materials and manufactured goods. Singapore in south-east Asia is the best example of this. Although within the area of the 'Third World', Singapore could quite easily be described as a developed rather than a developing place.

When a port was established on the island by the British in 1819, Singapore had a population of only 500; now it is a port and industrial city, business centre and independent country of 2 250 000 people. At first, its importance as a port was to export rubber and tin produced in Malaysia. However, much of its growth during the 20th century has been due to its excellent position within south-east Asia (see Figure 7.17).

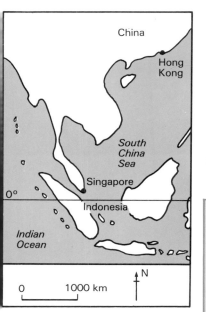

Fig. 7.17
The position of Singapore

Fig. 7.18
The port of Singapore

Tonnage of goods handled (1975)	
Oil	37 300 000 tonnes
General cargoes	14 500 000 tonnes
Total	51 800 000 tonnes

Number of ships handled

In 1975, 40 357 ships arrived at and departed from the port. There are 200 ships in the port each day, with a ship arriving or leaving every 13 minutes.

Port facilities

Oil is handled at terminals by the refineries which are mostly on islands. General cargoes are handled at six 'gateways', which include a large container port. Some ships anchor offshore and transfer cargoes to lighters (barges).

Exercise 7.9

(a) On an outline map of the world mark Singapore and the following major ports: Hong Kong, Djakarta, Manila, Tokyo, Seoul, Shanghai and Brisbane. Name the continents and oceans. Mark and name the Suez Canal. Then mark the shipping routes from each of these ports to Europe via the Suez canal. (Join the routes where they come close together.)

(b) On your map name the Persian Gulf and Japan and in a second colour mark the route taken by oil tankers between these two places.

(c) In the key to your map label the first group of routes, *'General cargo routes between Europe and Asia'* and the route in (b) *'Major oil tanker route'*. Give the map a suitable heading.

On your map you will notice that the routes in the first group focus at Singapore. Because of this Singapore has become an important *entrepôt*, a port which deals in trade between countries other than the one in which the port is located. For example, rubber may come into Singapore from Indonesia and be sent out to a European country.

Singapore became separate from Malaysia as an independent state in 1965. It was feared that Malaysia might divert some of its trade to its own ports and that other Asian countries would send their goods directly to Europe or North America, missing out Singapore. A few years later the British gave up their naval base at Singapore which employed 30 000 people on the island. Because of these developments, Singapore has developed manufacturing industry on a large scale. However, the fears that Singapore would become less important as a port have proved to be unjustified. Only Rotterdam, New York and Yokohama (Japan) handle greater amounts of cargo than Singapore. Figures 7.18, 7.19 and 7.20 give an idea of the port's importance. In fact, the recent growth of industry has helped the port to keep its importance.

Main imports
Oil, metal ores, metals, machinery, vehicles and other transport equipment, construction materials.

Main exports
Oil products, rubber, timber, chemicals, electronic and electrical goods, precision machinery, textiles, processed foods.

Free port
Jurong port is a free-trade zone. This means that firms can import materials and export goods made from them, without having to pay customs duties.

Fig. 7.19
Keppel Wharves—the largest of
the port of Singapore's 'gateways'. Here, up to 31 ships can
be accommodated

Fig. 7.20
Singapore's container terminal.
Notice the large area used for
stacking containers

Exercise 7.10

(a) Why would the countries of south-east Asia wish to export
goods directly from their own ports instead of through Singapore?
(b) Look at the information in Figure 7.18. What differences are
there in the types of goods exported between Mombasa, a typical
large African port, and Singapore?
(c) Figure 7.19 shows cargo being handled by the ships' own
derricks (cranes). The container terminal shown in Figure 7.20 is
typical of the most modern way of handling general cargo. What
advantages have the methods shown in Figure 7.20 over those
shown in Figure 7.19?

Oil refining is the most important industry in Singapore (Figure
7.21). This industry, which produces petrol, other fuels, lubricating
oils and raw materials for the chemical industry, is based on Singapore's position. It has been further helped by the production of oil in
south-east Asia itself. 40 million tonnes of oil are processed each year
but only 4 million tonnes are used in Singapore itself. The rest is
exported as far as Japan, Australia and New Zealand.

Exercise 7.11

(a) Look at an atlas map of Asia. Most of the oil
refined in Singapore comes from the Middle
East. Explain why large oil companies find
Singapore an excellent position for refining
Middle Eastern oil and then distributing the
products to the countries of eastern Asia and
Australasia.
(b) Figure 7.21 shows an oil refinery built on
one of Singapore's offshore islands. What disadvantages has such a site? Why would such a site
be less of a problem for Singapore than for a
country such as Britain?
(c) Suggest why Singapore is a major centre for
repairing ships, in particular oil tankers.

Fig. 7.21
An oil refinery on the offshore
island of Pulau Bukum

Fig. 7.22
Singapore's manufacturing
industries

Industry	Sales (1975) £ million
Metals and engineering	164
Shipbuilding and repairing	250
Oil refining, chemicals, plastics	870
Electronic and electrical goods	284
Photographic and optical equipment	30
Timber processing	63
Food and drinks	197
Textiles and clothing	103
Other industries	613
Total sales	2574

Singapore has many factories producing goods typical of those made in the developed countries rather than in the Third World. About 60% of her factories' production is exported, another unusual feature. Many of the factories are owned by American, European and Japanese companies who were attracted to Singapore by: (1) a well-educated labour force with wage rates below those of America and Europe; (2) the use of English as the main business language; (3) the country's position; (4) financial help from the Singapore government.

Figure 7.22 gives details of Singapore's manufacturing industries. Notice the importance of the oil industries. Several of the industries require a large labour force (oil refining is an important exception) and so labour accounts for a large part of the final cost of the products, in the case of a camera about 45%. Such industries are known as *labour-intensive* industries.

Exercise 7.12

(a)   Which of the industrial groups listed in Figure 7.22 could be described as being labour-intensive?

(b)   Figure 7.23 shows a Rollei slide projector made in Singapore. Rollei is a West German firm with a reputation for making high quality cameras and projectors. In recent years the firm has suffered from the competition of Japanese companies who could produce goods of the same quality at a lower price. Rollei's answer to Japanese competition was to open a factory in Singapore. Can you suggest why?

(c)   Since Singapore became independent there has been a great increase in the number of office jobs in banks, shipping offices and insurance companies. What are the reasons behind this development? What links has it with the view of Singapore's Central Business District in Figure 7.24?

As Singapore has a large population for a small area of land and has been developing rapidly, planning how land should be used has been a major problem. Industry, new housing to replace slums, and recreational activities all need space on which to expand. Figure 7.25 is a land-use map of Singapore. Four important developments since 1960 are shown in Figure 7.26. The first, third and fourth of these developments have not been marked on Figure 7.25 nor has the largest of the new housing estates.

Fig. 7.23 (below-left)
Fig. 7.24 (below-right)
Singapore's Central Business District

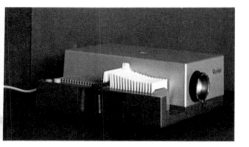

88

(a)

(b)

(c)

(d)

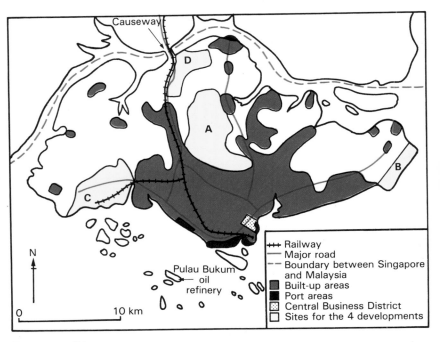

Fig. 7.25 Singapore

Fig. 7.26
(a) The construction of a large new industrial and port area together with a new town
(b) The construction of large new housing estates to rehouse people from overcrowded areas near the centre of the city
(c) The preservation of an area of forest as a nature reserve, water reservoir area and parkland
(d) The building of a new airport on land reclaimed from the sea

Exercise 7.13
(a) Trace the outline of the main island of Singapore from Figure 7.25. Also shade in the built-up area and the outlines of areas A, B, C and D.
(b) On your map mark where you would site (given the choice of areas A, B, C and D) the four new developments. Carefully consider all information on the map when making your decisions.
(c) Write a paragraph to explain your choice of sites.

Summary

The ports of developing countries were generally first developed by European countries who wished to obtain the products of these areas. As the exports of the developing countries and their demand for manufactured goods have increased, so has the importance of their ports. Modern shipping methods and the development of transport routes inland have meant that trade has become concentrated at certain major ports. Often there are problems of congestion at ports with large hinterlands. An important development has been the growth of specialised ports handling minerals in very large quantities. Some ports have become entrepôts. A select few have become centres of growth for modern industry and commerce, with important links across the globe.

8 Developing the land

In Chapters 2, 3 and 4 we saw that man adapts his use of the land to the environment both in his choice of crops and in his farming methods. For hundreds of years he has tried to overcome the problems or difficulties of the various environments in which he lives. The need to overcome such problems is particularly great today as the world's population is rising so quickly. Figure 8.1 shows a range of ways in which man has attempted to overcome environmental difficulties and increase the production of crops from the land.

Exercise 8.1

Figure 8.2 lists the methods of developing the land shown in the photographs. Make a copy of the table and in the second column write down the aims of the various methods. In the remaining columns indicate with ticks where you consider the methods would be helpful in the three types of tropical environment in developing countries named at the top of the columns. Some, of course, may not be of use in any tropical environment.

Method	Aim of method	Where the method would be useful		
		Tropical rain forests	Tropical highlands	Hot deserts
Irrigation Machinery Terracing Fertilisers Glasshouses Pesticides				

Fig. 8.2 Some ways of developing the land

(e)

(f)

Fig. 8.1
Some ways of increasing production from the land:
a) Irrigation
b) Machinery
c) Terracing
d) Fertilisers
e) Glasshouses
f) Pesticides

Irrigation

Irrigation is one of the oldest and most important methods of overcoming the problems of the environment. It permits farming to take place in arid areas with little or no rainfall and enables farmers in semi-arid areas to grow crops in the dry season and widen the range of crops which they can grow. Figure 8.3 shows maps of three countries in which irrigation has been practised for thousands of years. In each country there are large areas of desert or semi-desert where farming relies on water from large rivers which rise in areas of heavier rainfall.

90

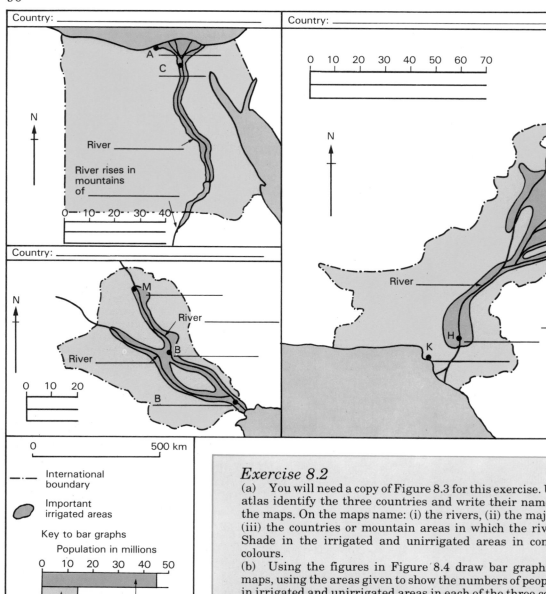

Country: _____

Country: _____

N

0 10 20 30 40 50 60 70

N

River _____

River rises in
mountains
of _____

0   10   20   30   40

River _____

Rivers rise
in

_____ mountains

Country: _____

N

River _____

River _____

0 10 20

0   500 km

— · — International
boundary

Important
irrigated areas

Key to bar graphs

Population in millions

0   10   20   30   40   50

Population
of
unirrigated
areas

Population
of
irrigated
areas

Fig. 8.3

Fig. 8.4
Population distribution in
Egypt, Iraq and Pakistan

Exercise 8.2

(a) You will need a copy of Figure 8.3 for this exercise. Using an atlas identify the three countries and write their names above the maps. On the maps name: (i) the rivers, (ii) the major cities, (iii) the countries or mountain areas in which the rivers rise. Shade in the irrigated and unirrigated areas in contrasting colours.

(b) Using the figures in Figure 8.4 draw bar graphs on the maps, using the areas given to show the numbers of people living in irrigated and unirrigated areas in each of the three countries. Shade in the bars to match the shadings you have used on the maps to show the two types of area.

(c) Briefly state the relationship between the distribution of population and the distribution of irrigated land in the three countries. In which country is the relationship most marked?

	Population living in irrigated areas	Population living in unirrigated areas
Egypt	37.5 million	0.5 million
Iraq	11 million	1 million
Pakistan	60 million	13 million

(Most of the towns in these countries are in the irrigated areas.)

Irrigation in Egypt
Traditional methods

Fig. 8.5
A Saqia

The waters of the Nile in Egypt have, until recent times, been used for irrigation in two ways. The first was by making use of the river's summer floods. In August and September, following the heavy summer rainfall in the Ethiopian Highlands, the Nile overflowed its banks and flooded the fields on its flood plain, at the same time depositing a layer of fertile silt (mud) over the land. As the flood level fell, the damp fields were planted with crops, mainly wheat and barley, which grew during the winter. In spring, after the harvest, fields remained dry and bare, awaiting the next floods. A clear disadvantage of farming under these conditions was that only one crop could be grown in a year, although temperatures were high enough for growth throughout the year. Also, crops might not have enough moisture during the later period of their growth, just before harvesting. The trapping of the flood water in the fields by constructing earth banks around them helped to save some extra water. This method is known as *basin irrigation*.

A second way to make use of the Nile's water, especially when it was not in flood, was to use various simple methods of lifting water out of the river, or from a short canal leading from it, on to the fields (Figure 8.5). These methods continue to be used today together with small diesel or electric pumps. Land very near to the river could therefore be used for all or most of the year.

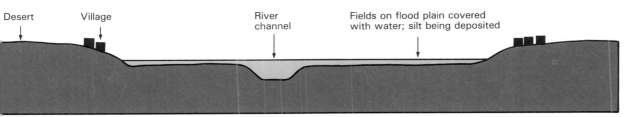

Desert · Village · River channel · Fields on flood plain covered with water; silt being deposited

Fig. 8.6
Cross-section of the Nile Valley, showing the water level as it used to be in late summer

Exercise 8.3
Figure 8.6 shows a diagrammatic cross-section of the Nile Valley. It shows the river level as it used to be in late summer when the Nile was in flood.
(a) Make a copy of the section, including the labels.
(b) Draw the section again, but show the level of the Nile as it used to be in winter. Label the use of the fields.
(c) Under the second section say when the crops would be harvested and what the state of the fields would have been during the summer.

Perennial irrigation
During the 20th century, Egypt's population has increased rapidly. Figure 8.7 shows how the population has almost trebled between 1920 and 1975. As we have seen, almost all the population lives in the Nile Valley and relies on irrigated farming for food, whether living in the country or in the towns. Dams or barrages have been built across the Nile so as to hold back flood water and then release it slowly throughout the drier months. As a result crops could be grown in the dry spring and early summer besides in winter, and so help to provide

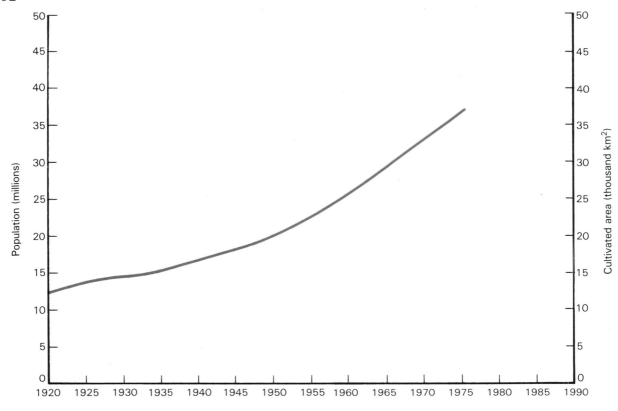

Fig. 8.7
Egypt's population growth

for the extra population. Irrigation throughout the year is known as *perennial irrigation*. However, the barrages and dams were rather small and trapped silt behind them so reducing the amount of water which could be stored (Figure 8.8). The only immediate solution was to let the main flood waters carrying much silt through the gates in the dams and then begin to store water in November when the river was falling and carrying less silt. However, if a year's flood period was short it meant that not enough water would be trapped for the following dry months.

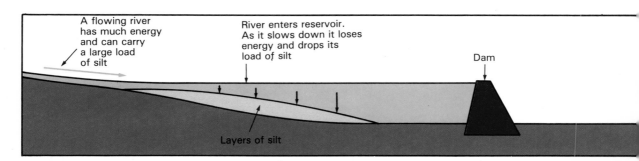

Fig. 8.8
How silt is trapped in a reservoir behind a dam

The Aswan High Dam

The conversion of some land from basin to perennial irrigation still did not meet the needs of the increasing population. As a result, the huge Aswan High Dam has been built so as to form a reservoir 500 km long to store all the water needs from one year to the next. Enough water is stored to irrigate land that was previously desert

Some new irrigated land has been used to produce cash crops such as cotton. At the dam, the fall of water is used to generate electricity for industry. Figure 8.10 gives figures for Egypt's cultivated area during the 20th century; for recent years, figures are also given for what the area would have been without the dam and small schemes using water from wells to the west of the Nile Valley.

Fig. 8.9
Irrigated land in the Nile Valley

Year	Cultivated area (km²)	
	With the dam	Without the dam
1920	26 000	
1925	26 000	
1930	26 000	
1935	26 000	
1940	26 000	
1945	27 000	
1950	29 000	
1955	30 000	
1960	31 000	
1965	35 000	(32 000)
1970	38 000	(32 000)
1975	40 000	(33 000)
1980 (est)	41 000	(33 000)

Fig. 8.10
Egypt's
cultivated area

The problems of waterlogging and salinity in irrigated areas

As more water is used on the land, more will soak into the ground. Eventually the ground will become saturated with water and surplus water will not drain away. The result is *waterlogged soil,* in which crops will not grow properly.

When surplus water evaporates under the hot sun salts are brought to the surface. Crops cannot grow properly in soil suffering from excess *salinity.*

Exercise 8.4

(a) Make a copy of the graph in Figure 8.7 to show the population growth of Egypt. Then, using the axis on the right-hand side of the graph, draw a graph to show the increase in Egypt's cultivated areas, both with and without the Aswan High Dam and other schemes.

(b) The Aswan High Dam has expanded the area of cultivated land in Egypt almost to its limit. On your graph continue with dotted lines into the future:

(i) the area of cultivated land at the same level as 1980,

(ii) the population, by continuing the curve already plotted. What problem do the graphs show? Can you think of any solutions?

Other problems of the scheme have been that the building of the dam was very costly (help was obtained from USSR); silt which used to renew the fertility of the soils gets trapped in the reservoir; people who lived in the town of Wadi Halfa and over 40 villages now covered by the reservoir had to be resettled. Temples built by the Pharaohs of Egypt, thousands of years ago, also had to be moved. The disease of bilharzia, caused by the larva of a water snail entering the human body has spread. As the larva lives on blood, its victims lack energy and have their lives shortened. Also, on any irrigated land in a hot climate, problems of *salinity* and *waterlogging* may occur. Figure 8.11 explains these terms.

Land affected by salinity.

Fig. 8.11
The problems of waterlogging and salinity in irrigated areas

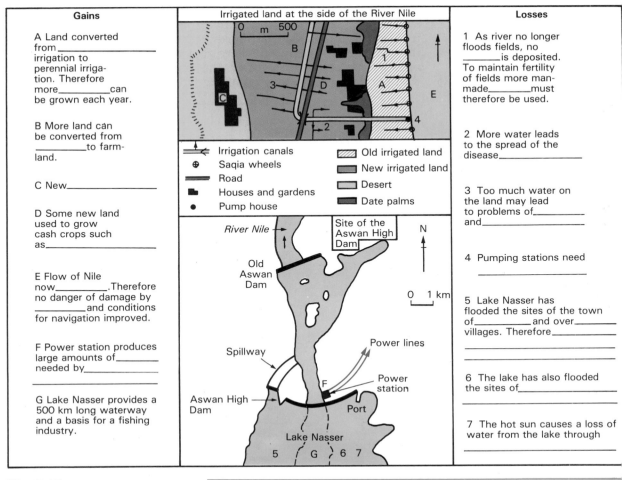

Gains

A Land converted from _____ irrigation to perennial irrigation. Therefore more _____ can be grown each year.

B More land can be converted from _____ to farmland.

C New _____

D Some new land used to grow cash crops such as_____

E Flow of Nile now_____.Therefore no danger of damage by _____ and conditions for navigation improved.

F Power station produces large amounts of_____ needed by_____ _____

G Lake Nasser provides a 500 km long waterway and a basis for a fishing industry.

Irrigated land at the side of the River Nile

Irrigation canals
Saqia wheels
Road
Houses and gardens
Pump house

Old irrigated land
New irrigated land
Desert
Date palms

River Nile
Site of the Aswan High Dam
Old Aswan Dam
Power lines
Spillway
Power station
Aswan High Dam
Port
Lake Nasser

Losses

1 As river no longer floods fields, no _____is deposited. To maintain fertility of fields more man-made_____must therefore be used.

2 More water leads to the spread of the disease_____

3 Too much water on the land may lead to problems of_____ and_____

4 Pumping stations need _____

5 Lake Nasser has flooded the sites of the town of_____ and over_____ villages. Therefore_____ _____ _____

6 The lake has also flooded the sites of_____ _____

7 The hot sun causes a loss of water from the lake through _____

Fig. 8.12
The effects of the Aswan High Dam

Exercise 8.5

Figure 8.12 includes a map of an area of land at the side of the Nile after the completion of the Aswan High Dam and a map of the dam site. Next to the maps the various gains and losses of the scheme have been listed in incomplete form. Divide your page into two columns headed 'Gains' and 'Losses'. Then copy the lists given in Figure 8.12 into the columns, filling in all the blank spaces.

The Green Revolution

Irrigation is a rather spectacular method of developing the land. Other developments are as important. They may well play a part in the organisation of newly irrigated areas.

Figure 8.13 shows a ricefield in Indonesia. If you look carefully you will notice that the rice in the left foreground is healthy looking and standing upright. However, the rice in the right background has been beaten down by a rainstorm. The healthy-looking rice is a newly developed type. It also has the advantage of being a high-yielding variety. The introduction of such a type of rice into a country enables the amounts of crop production to be increased without having to extend the cultivated area.

Fig. 8.13

Fig. 8.14
The position of Java

During the 1950s and 1960s, new types or strains of rice, wheat, millet and maize were developed, giving more than double the yields of traditional strains. These great increases depend, however, on large amounts of fertiliser and regular water supplies. Because the new strains are easily affected by pests and diseases, pesticides are also needed. The new strains grow and ripen more quickly than old strains and it is often possible to practise double cropping in a year (growing two crops where only one was grown before). Success with the new strains has led to the movement being called the *Green Revolution*.

The Green Revolution in Indonesia

The island of Java (Figure 8.14) in Indonesia is very densely populated and the introduction of new types of rice has been very important in increasing food production. Farmers may often be suspicious of new methods and ideas so demonstration plots of rice were planted in key villages and farmers were brought to see the effects of using fertilisers and new types of rice. Figure 8.15 is a photograph of a demonstration plot which shows clearly the effect of using fertilisers.

Java is a hilly island and because of the pressure of population the slopes at the side of the flat valley floors must be cultivated. Erosion of the soil by the rain has been a problem on these slopes and so farmers must be trained in careful farming and in maintaining terraces on the slopes. Only then can the Green Revolution be successful. Figure 8.16 shows rice cultivation in Java. Notice that traditional methods are still used in the fields.

Fig. 8.15
The effect of using fertiliser. Only the rice on the right-hand side of this demonstration plot has been fertilised

Fig. 8.16
Rice cultivation in Java:
a) Ploughing
b) Harrowing (smoothing) the flooded paddy field
c) The rice is transported from nursery beds and then fertiliser is applied
d) Hand weeding
e) Carrying the rice home after harvesting

Fig. 8.17
Flooded rice terraces in Java

Year	Average yield (kg/ha)
1961	247
1966	358
1968	546

Fig. 8.18
Wheat yields in the Ludhiana District of the Punjab, India

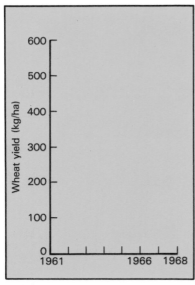

Fig. 8.19
Increasing wheat yields in the Ludhiana District of the Punjab, India

Fig. 8.21
A year's farming in a Punjab village before the Green Revolution

Exercise 8.6
(a) If you were an Indonesian farmer brought to see the demonstration plot in Figure 8.15, what would your reaction be?
(b) Look at the photographs in Figure 8.16. Describe the stages involved in cultivating rice. Which job would not have been done before the Green Revolution?
(c) Figure 8.17 shows flooded rice terraces in Java. Explain why the work involved in building and maintaining these terraces has to be done with a greater amount of care than with terraces used for other crops. Suggest what problems the farmer has in cultivating terraces as opposed to fields on a flat valley floor.

The Green Revolution in India
The Indian government has introduced the new strains of crops in order to achieve its aim of making the country self-sufficient in cereals. They were introduced at first to areas where people were better educated and ready to adapt to several new ideas at once. Figure 8.18 shows how wheat yields have increased in the Ludhiana District of the Punjab.

Exercise 8.7
(a) Plot the figures shown in Figure 8.18 on a graph using the axes given in Figure 8.19.
(b) What will be the effect of increasing wheat yields on the total production of wheat?

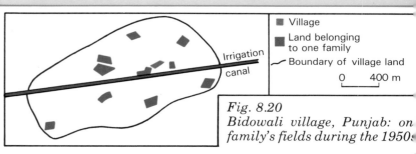

Fig. 8.20
Bidowali village, Punjab: on family's fields during the 1950s

Before the changes were introduced in the Punjab only a small proportion of the crops were grown for sale, most being consumed by the village people. Methods of farming were primitive. Farmers had their land split up into several scattered plots. Figure 8.20 shows the lands of one farmer in one village in the Punjab during the 1950s. This splitting up of a farmer's land is known as *land fragmentation*. Such patterns often grew up as a result of land being divided between a farmer's sons. Also, a farmer might wish to buy up some more land and could only obtain a plot some distance away. Some plots might become so subdivided that the tiny fragments left may be of little use for farming.

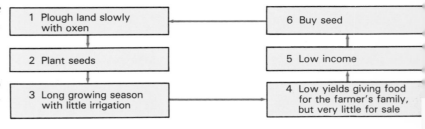

Exercise 8.8
Explain what problems the farmer who owned the land shown in the village in Figure 8.20 might have as a result of fragmentation. (Consider the tasks a farmer has to do, such as fencing land, travelling to his fields, carting manure, attending to irrigation and using machinery in the fields.)

The answer to land fragmentation is *consolidation*. This involves grouping a farmer's land into single compact units with straight edges. In the village shown in Figure 8.20 land had been reorganised by 1961 and new varieties of crop were able to be grown efficiently using carefully controlled irrigation and modern machinery.

Exercise 8.9
(a)   Under the heading *'Bidowali Village after Consolidation'*, draw just the outline of the village land from Figure 8.20 and mark the position of the village. The village land is owned by 20 farmers. On your outline map rearrange the land ownership so that all farmers have their land in one plot. Make sure that the plots have regular shapes with straight edges. Shade the land owned by the farmer shown on the first map. His new plot should include the largest fragment he had owned before.
(b)   What are the advantages of the new village map to the farmer?

The introduction of new strains of crops could only be successful with the improvement of irrigation methods and land consolidation. In spite of the increase in the output of crops there have been problems:
1.   new farm equipment is very expensive;
2.   fertiliser, pesticide and fuel prices have increased quickly each time oil prices have risen;
3.   electricity shortages mean that well irrigation and threshing machines often do not work.

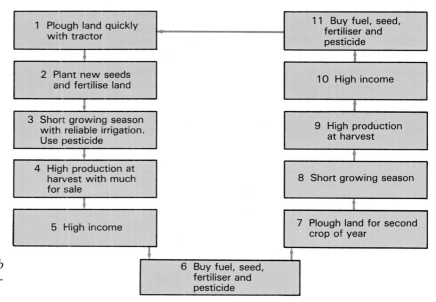

Fig. 8.22
A year's farming in a Punjab village after the Green Revolution

There have been other difficulties with the Green Revolution, in addition to those already mentioned. The new strains of rice are often not popular with customers because their grains are sticky and go mushy when cooked. Also, there are problems of storing the increased harvests and getting the crops to the towns along poor roads. Finally farmers in poorer parts of India than the Punjab have been unaffected by the Green Revolution. They have little or no money to spend on new methods, and the government is more likely to use its money to help farmers who will quickly adapt to using new techniques.

Mechanisation: not always a solution

The Green Revolution in India has involved the increasing use of machines. However, the introduction of tractors and other complex machines into developing countries does not necessarily solve the problems of farming in such areas. Tractors are very expensive to buy and run. If they break down, trained mechanics are needed; spare parts may not be available locally. The use of such *advanced technology* may not be particularly suitable for use in an area where there are lots of people needing jobs (and little money available to buy advanced machines with). People may lose jobs to machines. Methods which lie in between simple hand methods and advanced technology are often of greater real use. Such 'in between' methods are examples of *intermediate technology*. Figure 8.23 shows the three levels of technology used for preparing fields for crops. Some training is necessary for people to learn about making and repairing intermediate technology equipment, and money is needed to build workshops and buy materials. However, training can be short, materials are fewer and cheaper than with complex machines and jobs are provided for more people.

Fig. 8.23
Three ways of preparing land for crops
(a)   Simple—an African farmer using a hoe
(b)   Intermediate—an ox-drawn metal plough
(c)   Advanced—a four-wheel drive tractor with plough

(a)   *(b)*   *(c)*

(a)

(c)

(d)

(e)

(f)

Fig. 8.24
Three levels of technology for threshing and storing grain. Threshing grain (separating grain from straw)
(a) Simple—hand beating the crop
(b) Intermediate—a portable threshing machine
(c) Advanced—a combine harvester, which harvests and threshes the grain in one operation

Storing grain
(d) Simple—thatched grain-storage huts, not safe from attack by animals, insects and damp
(e) Intermediate—a ferro-cement silo. A steel and chicken-wire framework (background) is plastered with cement (foreground)
(f) Advanced—large concrete grain silos

Exercise 8.11
(a) Figure 8.24 shows simple, intermediate and advanced methods of threshing grain and storing grain. What are the disadvantages of the simple methods pictured? What are the advantages of the intermediate methods? What problems would be faced with the use of the advanced methods?
(b) Some people have said that intermediate technology is 'second best technology'. Why would this be said? Is this criticism fair? Explain your answers fully.

Improving transport links

Efficient transport is vital for the success of farming in developing countries. If a farmer has to walk for hours along rough tracks in order to get goods to market, he is wasting both time and energy. The rapidly growing towns of the developing countries require good transport links from the surrounding countryside if they are to receive food supplies in sufficient amounts and at reasonable prices. The good roads and the railway links which exist in developing countries have often been built to export minerals and cash crops. Export-crop production can expand only if such transport links are extended.

Good roads are needed for other purposes too: to bring building materials and farm equipment to villages, to enable health workers and agricultural experts to visit villages and to enable people to go to schools and hospitals.

We must remember, however, that road construction on a large scale may have less desirable side effects. In Chapter 2 we saw that the building of the Trans-Amazonica Highway had a serious effect on the well-being of the local Indian tribes.

Fig. 8.25
Roads in East Africa
(a)   (above-left) An unsurfaced road
(b)   (above-centre)   A   road crossing a dry river bed
(c)   (above-right) A tarred road

Exercise 8.12

(a)   Figure 8.25 shows roads in East Africa. What are the disadvantages of the roads in the first and second photographs? (Consider the types of vehicles which could use them, speed of transport, problems in the dry season, problems in the rainy season.) What advantages over the unsurfaced roads has the tarred road?.

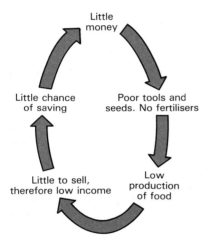

Fig. 8.26
The vicious circle of poverty

Fig. 8.27
Food and protein intakes in developed and underdeveloped countries

The vicious circle of poverty

For any improvements to take place, whether fairly simple or complex, money is needed. We have already seen that the improved methods of the Green Revolution have been most successful where the farmers were better off in the first place. Most people in the poorer countries cannot afford to buy the equipment, seeds and fertilisers that they need to improve their farming. As a result, their situation stays the same or becomes even worse. The pattern will repeat itself year after year. This vicious circle of poverty is shown in Figure 8.26.

As long as farmers are educated in the use of improved methods, money can break the vicious circle. Many farmers, however, will often find it impossible to save. In India, they will turn to the traditional money-lenders, who charge rates of interest as high as 100%. In paying back such loans they may well become poorer still. Governments can help farmers by lending money, but in many poor countries the government may be in a circle of poverty itself. There are, however, organisations which will make money available for projects in less developed countries. Aid may come from governments of developed countries, from international organisations such as the World Bank or the Common Market (EEC) and from voluntary organisations such as Oxfam or Christian Aid. If the aid is in the form of money, it may either be given (a grant) or be lent (a loan). Aid may also be in the form of equipment or volunteers and experts may go to the less developed countries to organise and help with projects.

(a)	Average food intake per person per day (calories)			
Developed countries		**Underdeveloped countries**		
United Kingdom	3140	Indonesia	1920	
USA	3270	India	2060	
France	3210	Brazil	2600	

(b)	Average protein intake per person per day (grammes)			
Developed countries		**Underdeveloped countries**		
United Kingdom	90	Indonesia	43	
USA	97	India	53	
France	104	Brazil	64	

Fig. 8.28
Some diseases affecting the
Third World

Exercise 8.13
(a)   Why would aid to help in irrigation schemes, road building or in training farmers be more helpful than gifts of grain and other foods?
(b)   On what occasions are direct gifts of food to poorer countries useful?

Cholera	Caused by infected excreta polluting water or food. Therefore spread by poor sanitation and polluted water supplies.
Typhoid	Spread in the same way as cholera.
Kwashiorkor	Due to a lack of protein. Affects children, causing swollen stomach and deterioration of the brain.
Rickets	Bone disease which affects children. Caused by a lack of Vitamin D, which is found in milk.
Beri-beri	Caused by a lack of Vitamin B, which is found in wheat, meat and eggs. Common in rice-eating areas and causes extreme weakness.
Malaria	Caused by a parasite which eats red blood cells. Spread by the anopheles mosquito.
Bilharzia	Larvae of a water snail enter the body and live on the victim's blood. Causes great weakness and reduces a person's life by nearly 20 years.
River blindness	Blindness caused by the similium fly, which lives in fast-flowing water.
Sleeping sickness	Weakening disease spread by the tsetse fly. Also severely affects cattle.

Other diseases include tuberculosis, influenza, meningitis (all passed on through the respiratory tract), yellow fever (spread by mosquitoes), smallpox, polio, measles (virus diseases), yaws and leprosy (both passed on by body contact).

Not enough food

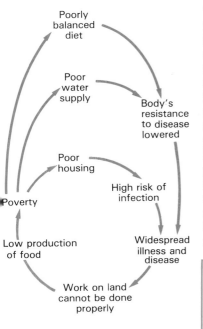

Fig. 8.29
The vicious circle of ill health

The basic reason for the need to develop the land in poorer countries is that large numbers of people in these countries do not receive enough food or enough of the right type of food. *Undernourishment* and *malnutrition* therefore result. Also, the number of people requiring food is rapidly increasing. Figure 8.27(a) contrasts the food intakes of the people in some developed and underdeveloped countries. The food intake has been measured in calories. A calorie is a unit which measures the energy value of food; we eat food so as to obtain energy. Calories can usefully measure total food intakes, but if the balance of people's diets is examined, the intakes of protein, carbohydrates and fats must be measured. Protein intake is especially important as protein is needed for growth and the formation of body tissues. Figure 8.27(b) gives protein intakes for the same countries as in the first table; notice that the contrast between developed and underdeveloped countries is even greater than with calorie intake. A balanced diet also requires a minimum amount of vitamins and minerals.

Exercise 8.14
(a)   Are people likely to use more physical energy in their work in developed or underdeveloped countries? Does the use of energy in these two groups of countries reflect the pattern of intake of energy as shown in Figure 8.27?
(b)   Find out what foods provide protein, carbohydrates and fats.

(a)

(b)

(c)

Fig. 8.30
(a)   A community health worker in India
(b)   A mobile clinic at a groundnut store in Senegal, West Africa
(c)   An adult nutrition class in Niger, West Africa

The problem of disease

People can only put the necessary energy into farming or other work if they are healthy. Many diseases are caused by the lack of a balanced diet. Also, a person suffering from undernourishment or malnutrition will have little resistance to other diseases. Figure 8.28 gives details of some of the diseases which are a great problem in poorer countries. The effect of disease is the vicious circle of ill health as shown in Figure 8.29. Good health reflects:
1.   A balanced diet.
2.   Pure water supplies, which help to prevent the spread of water-borne disease.
3.   Good housing conditions. Overcrowded living conditions provide a breeding ground for disease.
4.   Effective medical services for preventing and treating illness.

The provision of a better diet, water supplies, housing and medical services can break the vicious circle of ill health. We have already seen that there are problems in providing a better diet. The other improvements are also expensive and difficult to carry out. A safe, piped water supply is very expensive, so second-best schemes using tanks and wells and the education of people in how they use water must be adopted. Providing better houses and arrangements for getting rid of sewage is very expensive and only limited success has been achieved.

Modern medicine has helped to bring about the rapid decline in the death rate in the Third World and has also helped to cause the population explosion. Yet medical services are still inadequate and are often concentrated in the towns. Vaccination against diseases and the spraying of swamps where malaria-carrying mosquitoes breed have been important in reducing disease. The training of medical workers who can treat common complaints, give vaccinations and give health education has played an important role in many countries and can help to make up for the shortage of doctors (Figure 8.30).

Exercise 8.15
(a)   On the left-hand side of your page make a copy of Figure 8.29 to show the vicious circle of ill health. On the right-hand side of your page, list the four ways in which the circle may be broken. Link each of these ways by bold arrows to the points where they can break the vicious circle.
(b)   Describe the three scenes in Figure 8.30. In each case explain how the vicious circle of ill health is being attacked.

Summary

Increasing food production from the land is one of the most pressing needs of the developing countries. Irrigation allows the area of cultivated land to be extended into dry areas. Most ways of developing the land, however, involve increasing production from land already cultivated. This can be done by the introduction of new types of crops, the use of fertilisers and the development of improved ways of working the land. At the same time farmers must be trained, land formed into units large enough to work, storage facilities built and transport links improved. All this requires large amounts of money and hard work. Too many people in the developing countries, though, are trapped in the vicious circle of poverty and are affected by poor health.

9 Going to the city

Figure 9.1 shows eight cities in developing countries. There are great contrasts as far as housing, other buildings, transport and people's way of life are concerned. Some could quite easily be scenes in cities in developed countries, others show features which are typical of the Third World only.

Fig. 9.1

(a)

(b)

(c)

(d)

(e)

(f)

(g)

(h)

Exercise 9.1
(a) What problems of cities in developing countries are suggested by the photographs in Figure 9.1?
(b) Would all the people living in developing countries be affected by the problems you have named in your answer to Question (a)? Explain your answer.

The world's major cities

The congestion of people and vehicles and the poverty shown in some of the photographs partly reflect the rapid growth of cities in developing countries. The poverty also reflects, of course, the general low standard of living in these countries.

City	Country	Population (millions)
1 New York	USA	12.3
2 Tokyo—Yokohama	Japan	8.6
3 London	UK	8.3
4 Shanghai	China	6.1
5 Chicago	USA	4.9
6 Paris	France	4.7
7 Calcutta	India	4.6
8 Moscow	USSR	4.4
9 Los Angeles	USA	4.0
10 Buenos Aires	Argentina	3.7
11 Leningrad	USSR	3.0
12 Philadelphia	USA	2.9
13 Bombay	India	2.8
14 Peking	China	2.7
15 Tientsin	China	2.7
16 Detroit	USA	2.7
17 Mexico City	Mexico	2.3
18 Rio de Janeiro	Brazil	2.3
19 West Berlin	Germany	2.1
20 Cairo	Egypt	2.1

City	Country	Population (millions)
1 Tokyo—Yokohama	Japan	27.0
2 New York	USA	16.0
3 Mexico City	Mexico	11.9
4 Shanghai	China	10.8
5 Sao Paulo	Brazil	10.6
6 Paris	France	9.9
7 Rio de Janeiro	Brazil	8.8
8 Calcutta	India	8.4
9 Buenos Aires	Argentina	8.4
10 Moscow	USSR	7.7
11 Peking	China	7.6
12 London	UK	7.2
13 Los Angeles	USA	7.0
14 Chicago	USA	7.0
15 Bombay	India	6.9
16 Seoul	South Korea	6.9
17 Cairo	Egypt	5.9
18 Jakarta	Indonesia	5.7
19 Philadelphia	USA	4.8
20 Tientsin	China	4.3

Fig. 9.2 (above-left)
The world's twenty largest cities in 1950

Fig. 9.3 (above-right)
The world's twenty largest cities in 1975

Thirty years ago, most of the world's large cities were outside the Third World. Figure 9.2 lists the world's twenty largest cities in 1950, together with their populations. There are nine representatives from the developing countries in the list. The list of the world's twenty largest cities for 1975 contains twelve from the Third World (Figure 9.3). Notice also that several of the major cities in the developed countries have shown relatively little growth since 1950 and the population of London has even declined. On the other hand, the Third World cities have clearly increased rapidly in size. Many are doubling their population every ten years. The ten fastest growing large cities in the world are all in the Third World (Figure 9.4).

	City	Country	Per cent increase each year
1	Dacca	Bangladesh	16
2	Guadalajara	Mexico	12
3	Lima	Peru	12
4	Kinshasa	Zaire	11
5	Seoul	South Korea	11
6	Addis Ababa	Ethiopia	10
7	Medellin	Colombia	9
8	Belo Horizonte	Brazil	9
9	Sao Paulo	Brazil	9
10	Madras	India	8

Fig. 9.4
The world's ten fastest-growing large cities

Fig. 9.5
Percentage population of major world regions living in urban areas

Percentage of population living in urban areas	Regions	Code letter to use on map
Over 70%	1. North America 2. Chile and Argentina 3. North-west Europe 4. Australia 5. Japan	A
50 to 70%	1. South America except Chile and Argentina 2. Mexico 3. Southern and Eastern Europe 4. USSR	B
25 to 50%	1. Central America except Mexico 2. North Africa (Morocco to Egypt) 3. Central Africa (Gabon, Zaire, Zambia) 4. Republic of South Africa 5. Western Asia (Turkey to Pakistan including Saudi Arabia)	C
Less than 25%	1. The rest of Agrica 2. Southern and Eastern Asia (including India, China and Indonesia)	D

Exercise 9.2
(a)   On an outline map of the world:
(i)   Shade in the area of the Third World countries (refer back to Figure 1.2);
(ii)   mark with a dot and name the twenty largest cities in the world;
(iii)   mark with an asterisk (*) and name the ten fastest growing large cities in the world;
(iv)   Figure 9.5 gives the percentage population living in urban areas of major world regions; use the code letters A to D, as given in Figure 9.5, on the correct regions on your map;
(v)   add a key to your map so as to explain all the symbols used.
(b)   Study your completed map carefully. Regions with a high percentage of people living in cities are more *urbanised* than those with a low percentage.
(i)   Are the Third World countries more or less urbanised than the average for the world?
(ii)   Considering your answer to the last question, would you consider the Third World countries to have a relatively great or small share of the world's very large cities?
(iii)   All the ten most rapidly growing cities in the world are in the Third World. Considering this fact, in what way would you think that the urbanisation figures for the major regions might change in the future?

Urbanisation: moving to the cities

Although the Third World countries are generally less urbanised than the other countries, we must remember that two-thirds of the world's population live in the Third World. This means that in terms of total numbers of people, the population of the Third World urban areas is very high. More than one person in two of the world's town and city dwellers live in the Third World. This proportion is increasing all the time and by the end of the century may be two out of three.

We have seen that the town and cities of developing countries are growing rapidly. This is partly due to the fact that populations of developing countries show a high rate of growth generally. Figure 9.6 gives the total population of India for 1921 and 1971 together with the number of people living in cities of 100 000 or more for the same years. Notice how much both figures have risen over the 50 years.

	Total population (millions)	Population living in cities of 100 000 or more (millions)
1921	252	7
1971	547	61

Fig. 9.6 (above)
India's population

Fig. 9.7 (below)
Going to the city

Exercise 9.3
Calculate the percentage of the total population of India who live in cities of 100 000 or more for 1921 and 1971. Record your answer in the form of a bar graph, giving it the heading 'Urbanisation in India'.

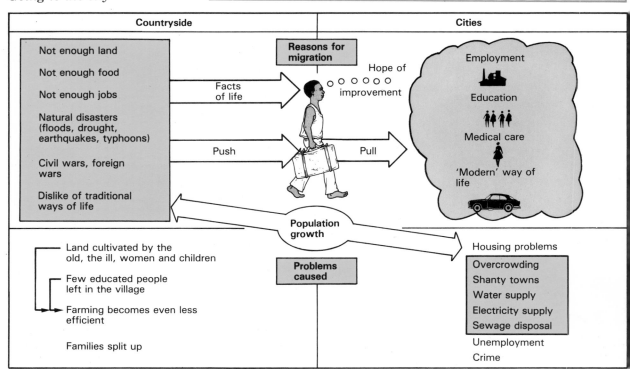

Such an increase in the percentage of a country's population living in urban areas is known as *urbanisation*. It is caused by the movement of people to the towns from the rural areas. The developed countries went through a phase of rapid urbanisation in the 19th century; industry was growing rapidly and needed large amounts of labour. The reasons for people moving to the urban areas of the developing countries are not so simple. Industry is growing, but not as fast as, for example, in Britain in the 19th century. Also modern industry is more automated and usually requires relatively little labour compared with the factories of the last century.

As a result, many people who move to the cities do not find work. Of course, many go to the city hoping to find work, but there are other reasons for going to the cities as well. Figure 9.7 shows the process of urbanisation in the Third World and indicates the other reasons for it. The diagram also shows that the growth in population of the Third World cities leads to many problems. The Third World cities are growing especially quickly in countries which are relatively poor, unlike England in the 19th century. As a result, the problems of housing, supplying water and electricity, and providing sewers and roads become so great that normal planning is impossible.

Fig. 9.8
Shanty town, Calcutta

Exercise 9.4
(a) What are the advantages and disadvantages for the countryside of the movement to the cities? On the whole, do you consider the movement to the cities good or bad for the country areas?
(b) Describe the cities' problems caused by their rapid growth of population. Are there any advantages which help to offset these problems? If so, what are they?

Fig. 9.9
Pavement bicycle repairer, Delhi

Shanty towns

The growth of shanty towns is a distinctive feature of Third World cities. A newcomer to a city will arrive with little or no money, so he could not afford to rent reasonably good quality housing. If he had a little money he might be able to rent a share of a small room in a slum area, if he could find one. An alternative, especially if he has a family, would be to become a squatter on land at the edge of the city and build a rough shack out of cardboard, packing cases or any other material he could find. Shanty towns such as those shown in Figure 9.8 are found in practically all the Third World cities. In these areas, there are no surfaced roads and the shacks lack water supplies, electricity and sewage facilities. Many of the people living in the shanty towns do not have permanent jobs. Many work as refuse collectors, car cleaners, shoe shiners, night watchmen, gardeners and lottery ticket sellers, all being jobs which provide minor services for more prosperous people (Figure 9.9). In many Indian cities, the housing and employment situation is so bad that a lot of people have to live and sleep on the streets (Figure 9.10). In Calcutta 600 000 people exist in such conditions.

How can the squatter problem be solved? The method used by developed countries in dealing with slum areas has been to demolish the slums and build new houses or flats. Let us have a look at some solutions which have been attempted in the developing countries.

Fig. 9.10
Pavement dwellers, Bombay

Fig. 9.11 (top-left)
People living in overcrowded housing areas lack basic services. Here, water is being delivered in Calcutta

Fig. 9.12 (top-right)
Hong Kong: overcrowded Chinese tenements

Fig. 9.13 (bottom-left)
Hong Kong: shanty town with new flats behind

Fig. 9.14 (bottom-right)
Hong Kong: Shatin New Town

Large-scale redevelopment

In many Third World cities shanty towns and other slum areas have been bulldozed and flats built to house at least some of their inhabitants. Figures 9.12 and 9.13 show overcrowded housing conditions in Hong Kong. The policy of the Hong Kong Government has been to clear the slum tenements and shanty towns and to rehouse people on large new estates and in new towns away from the city. Between 1953 and the end of 1976 nearly 1.9 million people were rehoused. There is a shortage of land in crowded Hong Kong and so almost all the new housing has to be in multi-storey blocks. Figure 9.14 shows part of the new town of Shatin under construction. It is being built on land reclaimed from the sea. In the background of the photograph new building land is being formed by terracing the hillsides.

Most of the old tenement buildings as shown in Figure 9.12 have now gone but many shanty towns still exist in Hong Kong, despite the huge housing construction programme. Large-scale redevelopment has only been possible because of Hong Kong's rapidly expanding industrial wealth; many Third World governments cannot afford to undertake such schemes. Also, many people cannot afford the rents for the flats and the population of the cities continues to grow. The result is that more shanty towns grow up.

Other solutions

Figure 9.15 shows low-cost housing under construction in Colombia, South America. Here housing is being built by the people of a poor neighbourhood with materials provided by the government. Such 'self-help' schemes still require considerable amounts of money and again seldom keep pace with the demand for housing from the rapidly increasing population of the cities.

Fig. 9.15 (top-left and right) Colombia: self-help housing under construction

Fig. 9.16 (bottom-left) Poor quality housing at Ashaiman, Tema in Ghana

Fig. 9.17 (bottom-right) A better quality house at Ashaiman, Tema

Many governments have been forced to adopt second-best solutions. On the edge of Tema in Ghana the government has attempted to guide the development of home-made houses by laying out the lines of streets and selling small building plots. As you can see in Figures 9.16 and 9.17 the quality of the houses which have been built varies greatly.

Exercise 9.5

(a) What are the advantages and disadvantages of large-scale redevelopment of shanty towns?

(b) Why are many countries unable to redevelop shanty towns on such a large scale as in Hong Kong?

(c) What are the advantages and disadvantages of self-help housing schemes?

(d) What problems would there be in providing roads and services for already existing shanty towns?

(e) Suggest what advantages there are in guiding the growth of housing areas, as on the edge of Tema, rather than letting people build their homes anywhere.

Fig. 9.18
Closely packed buildings in Hong Kong

The structure of cities

Cities are densely populated places. With over-crowded housing conditions commonplace, the cities of the developing countries are usually far more densely populated than the cities we are familiar with. If there is a shortage of land for building, as in Hong Kong, then very high population densities will occur. In parts of Hong Kong, as many as 230 000 people live in one square kilometre; Figure 9.18 shows the appearance of such an area.

Fig. 9.19 Kano, Nigeria

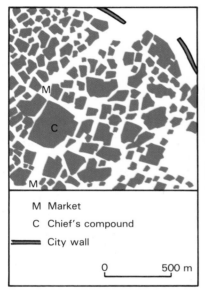

M Market
C Chief's compound
━━ City wall

0   500 m

Fig. 9.20
Plan of part of an old Nigerian city

Let us have a closer look at the structure of the densely populated cities of the developing countries. In many of these countries cities already existed when the European countries began to trade with them and to set up colonies. Figure 9.19 shows views of Kano in Nigeria looking very much the same as it did when Nigeria came under British rule in the last century. The old Nigerian cities consist of a collection of compounds each of which is occupied by a large family. The streets appear to be merely the spaces which have been left between the buildings (Figure 9.20).

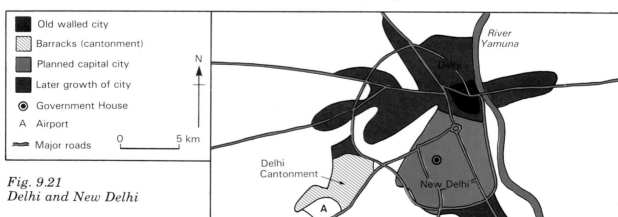

■ Old walled city
▨ Barracks (cantonment)
▨ Planned capital city
■ Later growth of city
◉ Government House
A Airport
〰 Major roads

0   5 km

Fig. 9.21
Delhi and New Delhi

Where large cities such as these already existed, the Europeans would often add to them their own sections containing offices, homes and industries. Figure 9.21 is a map of Delhi in India, with an old-established walled town and newer sections built by the British. New Delhi was built as the capital city of India in the early 20th century.

Exercise 9.6
(a) Look at Figure 9.19. What difficulties would the Europeans have had in establishing their offices and other buildings in these old sections of the cities?

(b) Describe the appearance and arrangement of buildings in Kano. What appears to have come first, the buildings or the streets?

Fig. 9.22
Housing in a British city: Nottingham

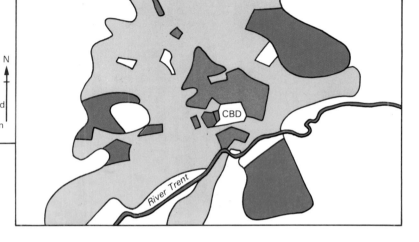

CBD Central Business District

⬛ Low quality housing

⬛ High quality housing

◻ Rest of built-up area, including medium quality housing.

The map is of Nottingham in 1965. Since then much of the low quality housing has been cleared and new housing built.

0   5 km

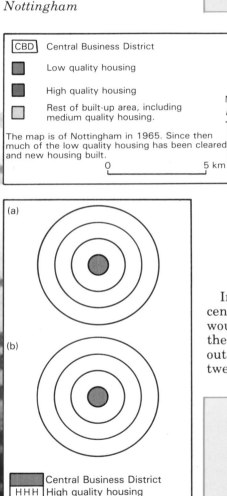

(a)

(b)

Central Business District
HHH High quality housing
MMM Medium quality housing
LLLL Low quality housing

Fig. 9.23
Simplified patterns of housing zones in cities
(a) *In an old Third World city*
(b) *In a British city*

In the old parts of Kano the richer people would live near the centre, close to the ruler of the city in his palace. The poorer people would live towards the edge of the town. During the 20th century, in the larger cities of many countries the richer people have often moved out of the central areas and their houses have been divided up between several poor families.

Exercise 9.7
(a) Suggest why, as cities have grown larger, richer people have moved out of the central areas.

(b) In Delhi, to which section of the city might the richer people move?

(c) Figure 9.22 is a simplified map of a British city. Where are the poorer quality houses found? Where are the high quality houses found?

(d) The two diagrams in Figure 9.23 represent zones of housing: (i) in an old Third World city, (ii) in a British city. In each case decide where low quality, medium quality and high quality housing would be found. Copy the diagrams and shade in the housing zones according to the key in Figure 9.23.

(e) Write a sentence to describe the main difference in the arrangement of housing zones in the diagrams you have drawn.

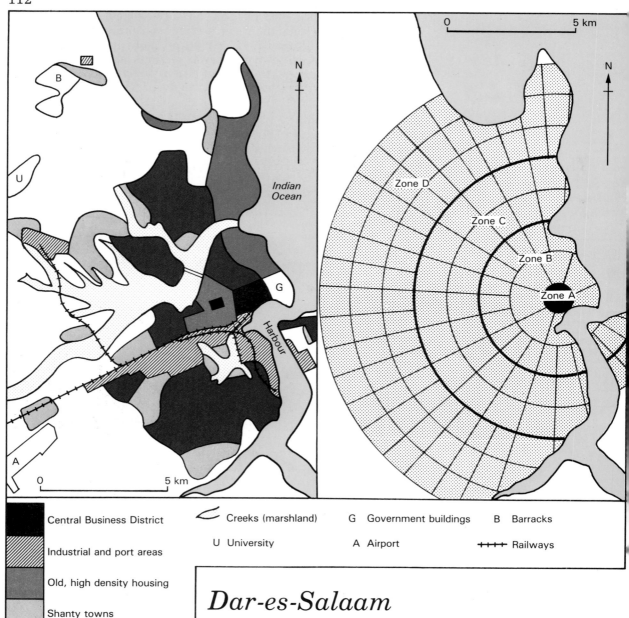

Central Business District

Industrial and port areas

Old, high density housing

Shanty towns

Mainly medium quality housing

High quality housing (low density)

Creeks (marshland)

U University

G Government buildings

A Airport

B Barracks

++++ Railways

Fig. 9.24 (above-left) Land-use map of Dar-es-Salaam, Tanzania

Fig. 9.25 (above-right) Outline for a simplified land-use map of Dar-es-Salaam

Dar-es-Salaam

Rapidly growing cities in developing countries have a structure which is a complicated mixture of traditional Third World cities and of cities in developed countries. Figure 9.24 is a land-use map of Dar-es-Salaam, the capital and largest city of Tanzania, East Africa. Until 1891, Dar-es-Salaam was very small, but in that year it became the capital of the country under the rule of Germany. The Germans put up government buildings on the sea front and built large houses nearby. Under German rule, and from 1916 under British rule, the city began to grow quickly as a port and as a centre for industry and commerce. Many Asians moved in to run shops and other businesses. In 1961 Tanzania became an independent country and since then Dar-es-Salaam has grown even more quickly. Squatters from the countryside have built shanty towns on the city's edge. Now it has a population of 517 000.

Exercise 9.8

(a)   The built-up area of Dar-es-Salaam is broken up into different sections. What features of physical geography are responsible for this?

(b)   In which part of the city would the British people involved in governing Tanzania have lived before independence. Explain your answer.

(c)   Many of the Asians live in the Central Business District. Why is this?

(d)   On a piece of tracing paper trace Figure 9.25, an outline for a simplified map of land use in Dar-es-Salaam. Position the tracing paper over Figure 9.24 and decide which land use covers most area in each separate space. Colour each space in according to the key to Figure 9.24

Fig. 9.26
Dar-es-Salaam, Tanzania

Your land-use map is made up of a series of zones between the part circles (A, B, C, D on Figure 9.25). Zone A is the Central Business District. Notice that the old, high density, poor quality housing is in Zone B, that Zone C has mainly medium quality housing and that Zone D has patches of both medium quality housing and of poor shanty towns. Industry and high quality housing are arranged in strips going out from the centre towards the edge of the city.

Exercise 9.9

(a)   Suggest why the industry and high quality housing areas lie in strips across the zones (consider what features shown on Figure 9.24 have affected their location).

(b)   Refer back to the diagrams you completed for Exercise 9.7(d) based on Figure 9.23. Is the distribution of the poor housing in Dar-es-Salaam (old, high density housing and shanty towns):

(i)   as in a British city;

(ii)   as in an old Third World city;

(iii) a mixture of the two diagrams?

Does the distribution of high quality housing have any similarity to the diagrams you completed?

(c)   Look at Figure 9.26 and compare it with the map of Dar-es-Salaam.

(i)   Which land-use zone is in the foreground? Which land-use zone can be seen most clearly in the background?

(ii)   In which direction was the camera pointing to take this photograph?

The development of manufacturing industry

We have seen that an important reason for the growth of cities in developing cities is the development of manufacturing industry

Fig. 9.27
Craft industries
(a) Weaving baskets
(b) Making sandals from old car tyres

People move to the cities in the hope of getting a job in a factory although, as we saw, many do not succeed because the rate of industrial growth is not as rapid as the rate of population increase.

Articles needed for farming, in the home and for clothing have been made in developing countries for hundreds of years, often in villages by craftsmen in their homes. Figure 9.27 shows some examples of such *domestic* or *craft* industries. Modern manufacturing industry in factories is a very recent development in most developing countries. Governments wish to develop industry in their countries in order to increase the wealth of the country and of their people. Development of industry will save spending so much hard-earned money on materials and manufactured goods from developed countries. Also industry provides work for people. Figure 9.28 lists the industries to be found in Tanzania. The list is typical of many developing countries. It includes industries in the following groups:

1. those producing building materials and oil products for industry and transport.
2. those making *consumer goods* (articles needed by people for themselves and their homes).
3. those producing goods for farming, fishing and transport.
4. those processing export crops.

Vegetable oil

Brewing

Sugar refining

Tobacco processing

Sisal twine and sacks

Instant coffee

Cotton textiles

Fish nets

Plywood

Radio assembly

Fruit canning

Razor blades

Shoes

Farm implements

Meat canning

Oil refining

Cement

Clothing

Bricks and tiles

Foam rubber

Tyres

Fertilisers

Soap

'Corrugated iron' sheets

Assembly of vehicles from kits

Fig. 9.28
Industries of Tanzania

Exercise 9.10

(a) Divide your page into four columns. Head the columns with the names of the four industrial groups given above. Re-arrange the list of Tanzania's industries into these columns.
(b) Look at the list of industries making consumer goods. What does it suggest about the prosperity of most Tanzanians? What types of consumer goods made in Britain do not appear in this list?
(c) Why is the development of industries producing building materials particularly important in developing countries?

You will notice that in the list, with the exception of those industries processing crops for export, the industries are producing goods needed inside Tanzania. In fact, Tanzania also exports some cement and products of the oil refinery to neighbouring countries. The list does not include one group of industries found in many developing countries—the smelting of metal ores—as Tanzania has no major mineral deposits. We saw in Chapter 6 that Zambia, a neighbour of Tanzania, has copper smelting as a major industry.

What is needed for industry to develop?

Figure 9.29 lists several things which are needed if industry is to develop in any country.

	Raw materials to make the manufactured goods from These may be minerals, crops or the products of other industries (for example, steel).
	A market, somewhere to sell the goods to This may be another industry which uses the goods to make something else or may be people in the case of industries making consumer goods. If people are relatively rich they will buy more goods and so the market will be relatively larger.
	Transport facilities, to bring in the materials and send out the finished goods Roads and railways will be needed together with port facilities for importing and exporting.
	Power supplies, to drive machinery and for heating purposes Coal, oil, gas or electricity may be used.
	A labour supply, to operate the factories Many people who will need only a small amount of training will be needed. In addition skilled workers, technicians, engineers and managers will be required.
£ £ £	Capital or money to build factories, buy machinery and train workers.

Fig. 9.29
Requirements for the development of industry

Exercise 9.11
Look at Figure 9.29.
(a) Which requirements for the development of industry will developing countries most easily be able to provide? Explain your answer carefully.
(b) Which requirements will developing countries have difficulty in providing? Again, explain your answer.

Choosing the right industries in a poor country

In developing industry a poor country must think carefully about the type of industry which should be encouraged. A large iron and steel works would produce more steel than a small country would need; in other words the market for the product is too small. We saw that Tanzania's consumer-goods industries make low-cost articles which are basic needs for the people. There would therefore be little point in building large factories to make cars and colour television sets for sale in Tanzania. A poor country, besides taking care in choosing which industries to develop, must also make sure that the *production methods* used are chosen carefully. For example, one developing country wished to expand the production of shoes. What it did and what happened is shown in Figure 9.30. Neither the country nor many of its people gained by this development. In this situation, as in developing agriculture, the use of *intermediate technology* rather than advanced technology would have been better. The 5000 shoemakers could have been supplied with simple sewing machines to stitch soles to the uppers in order to speed their work. More shoes would have been made and nobody would have lost their jobs. The plastic shoes had two important advantages over leather ones—they lasted longer and were cheaper—but it is unlikely that these advantages outweigh the problems caused by the new factory.

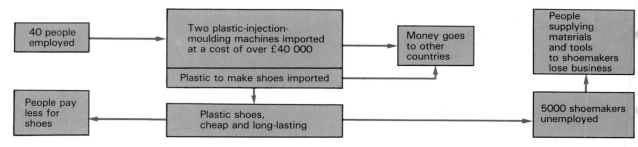

Fig. 9.30
What happened when a developing country wished to expand shoe production

Exercise 9.12
(a) Look at Figure 9.30. Which of the effects of the new shoe industry shown are losses. Which are gains?
(b) Listed below are several factories which a poor country with a fairly small population is considering building. Which of the factories would you consider to be useful to the country? Which ones would not? Give reasons for each of your choices.
Large car assembly plant; factory making farm implements; cement works; bicycle assembly plant; factory producing electronic goods; textile mill with highly automated equipment.

Some of the more prosperous developing countries have been able to develop industry on a large scale and are succeeding in increasing their wealth. Singapore, which we looked at in Chapter 7, is such a country. We will be having a look at some others in the next chapter.

Summary

The cities of the Third World are growing rapidly for two reasons: (1) the natural increase of population is high in these countries, and (2) people are moving from the countryside to the cities. The second reason means that the percentage of the population of developing countries who are city dwellers is rising; this process is known as urbanisation. Urbanisation rates are most rapid in the developing countries. Many people move to the cities because of poverty in the countryside and the hope that they may find work in factories in urban areas. The rapid growth of cities in the Third World has given rise to severe problems of housing and planning and to a pattern of land use which is different from cities in developed countries.

The development of industry has been a causal factor in the growth of cities. Many developing countries see this as a way of increasing their prosperity but face many difficulties in getting factories set up.

10 Growing wealth

Fig. 10.1

The sight of rich Arabs in London on business and shopping trips from the Middle East has become very common in recent years. Newspapers have reported Arabs buying up office buildings, hotels and expensive houses in London, and spending large amounts of money on luxury goods in expensive and fashionable shops. What is the reason lying behind this obvious wealth of people from a group of developing countries? Figure 10.1 provides the answer—oil. Oil has been produced in the Middle East for many years, but only recently has it led to a rapid build up of wealth. Figure 10.2 shows the location of the oil-producing countries and the amounts of oil produced by them. Notice the concentration of production around the shores of the Persian Gulf.

Fig. 10.2
Oil-producing countries of the Middle East

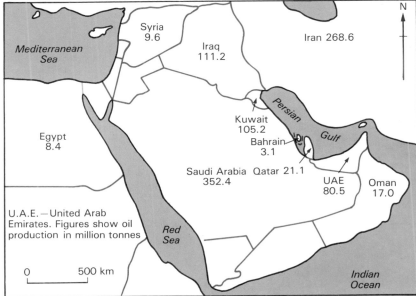

A leap into the 20th century

Before the wealth from oil was built up by the countries around the Persian Gulf, most of them were among the poorest and least developed countries of the world, with their people making a living from activities such as fishing, oasis cultivation and the grazing of livestock on poor desert pastures. Many people in the remoter areas still remain little affected by the modern world in contrast to those in the towns (Figure 10.3).

> *Exercise 10.1*
> Suggest how increasing wealth in the Middle East might affect the ordinary people in the area.

Fig. 10.3
A street scene in Dubai, United Arab Emirates

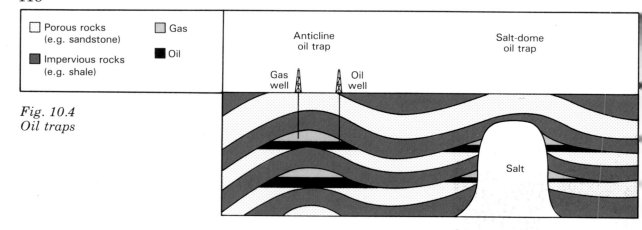

Fig. 10.4
Oil traps

The basic reason for the development of oil in the Middle East is the geology of the area—the fact that the rock structures contain vast reserves of oil and natural gas. Oil is formed from the decomposed remains of tiny sea creatures and plants which were buried in sand and mud on the sea bed. Pressure on the sand and mud from new layers of material above causes the loose materials to harden into layers (strata) of rock and the oil droplets are forced into the spaces or pores between the sand grains. The oil remains in the rocks where the strata are arranged so as to trap the oil underground. Figure 10.4 shows how oil occurs underground in geological structures known as *oil traps*. Notice that oil is found in porous rocks which have tiny pores to hold it and that these rocks are sandwiched between impervious rocks that will not allow any liquid to pass through them. If an area has anticlines and salt domes, it does not automatically mean

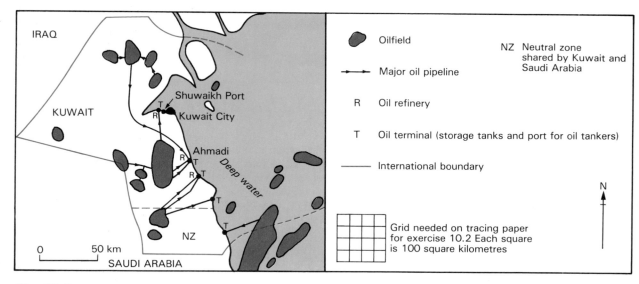

Fig. 10.5
Kuwait

that oil will be present.

Look at the map of Kuwait in Figure 10.5. Throughout the country, the geological structures suggest that oil may occur. The area covered by oilfields—where oil is actually present in amounts worth the expense of drilling—is relatively small.

Kuwait: an oil producing state

Kuwait is one of the world's leading oil producers, yet it covers only a small area and has a population of only about one million people. Drilling for oil started in 1938 and since then the oil industry has grown rapidly. The location of the main features of the country's oil industry are shown in Figure 10.5.

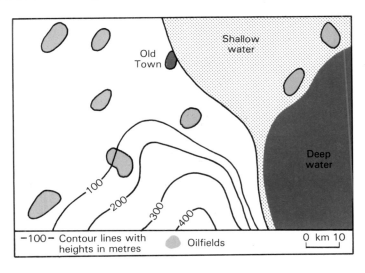

Fig. 10.6 (above-left)
An oil terminal
Fig. 10.7 (above-right)
An oil-producing area

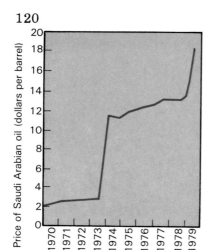

Fig. 10.8
Rising oil prices

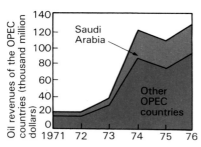

(OPEC is the Organisation of Petroleum Exporting Countries. Most OPEC countries are in the Middle East)

Fig. 10.9
Increasing wealth from oil

Fig. 10.10
Oil-producing countries of the Middle East

Exercise 10.4

Figure 10.7 is a map of an oil-producing area. On a copy of it mark the location of an oil terminal and port, an oil refinery and a new town. Join the oilfields to the terminals with pipelines (keeping their length as short as possible).

More money from oil

At the beginning of this chapter, it was said that the rapid build up of wealth from oil by the countries around the Persian Gulf has taken place quite recently. Oil prices have risen rapidly in recent years especially since 1973 (Figure 10.8). Rising oil prices have been responsible for large amounts of money moving into the Arab world (Figure 10.9) and the rapid economic development of the countries around the Persian Gulf. The oil-producing countries have been able to get higher prices for their oil by grouping themselves into an organisation known as OPEC (Organisation of Petroleum Exporting Countries), which bargains with the large oil companies from North America and western Europe. Those countries with a large oil production (see Figure 10.2) will clearly be receiving the largest share of the wealth from oil. However, a clearer idea of the benefits from oil to an individual country can be obtained if the production of oil is compared with the population of the country. Figure 10.10 includes oil-production and population figures for the Middle East oil producers. The third column of figures, oil production per head, is calculated by dividing oil production by population.

Country	Oil production, 1975 (million tonnes)	Population 1975 (millions)	Oil production per person (tonnes)	Average income per person, 1975 (£)	Letters for graph
Bahrain	3.1	0.3	10.3	1250	B
Egypt	8.4	38.1	0.2	140	E
Iran	268.6	33.9	7.9	648	In
Iraq	111.2	11.5	9.7	476	Iq
Kuwait	105.2	1.0	105.2	5532	K
Libya	71.5	2.4	29.8	1300	L
Oman	17.0	0.8	21.1	800	O
Qatar	21.1	0.1	211.0	6250	Q
Saudi Arabia	352.4	9.2	38.3	1242	SA
Syria	9.6	7.6	1.3	168	S
United Arab Emirates	80.5	0.3	268.4	8000	U

Exercise 10.5

(a) Draw the axes of a graph as shown in Figure 10.11. On the graph plot oil production per person against average income per person (listed in Figure 10.10) for each of the countries. Notice that a different scale has been used for the very high figures. Two examples have already been plotted on the graph. Use the letters given in Figure 10.10 to mark where each country should occur on the graph.

(b) Draw a *straight* line running as near as possible to all the points plotted on the graph. Such a line is a *best-fit line*.

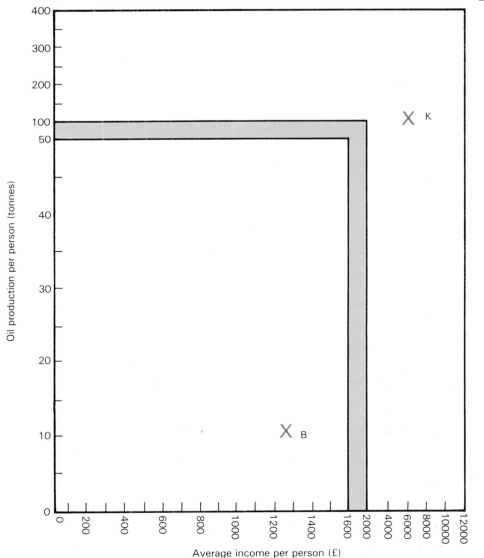

Fig. 10.11
The Middle East oil producers: graph of oil production per person against average income per person, 1975

Your graph will show that those countries with a high figure of oil production per head tend to have a high average income per head. There is, therefore, a *correlation* between the two sets of figures. Notice that some countries lie well away from the best-fit line. Such exceptions are called *residuals*. Notice that there is one very marked residual. Remember this country as we will be having a closer look at it later on.

Using the wealth from oil

Figure 10.12 shows some of the many ways in which the governments of the oil states have used the wealth from oil. The appearance of towns has been completely altered by the many large construction projects. Figure 10.13 shows how the port and town of Dubai, in the United Arab Emirates, has changed with the wealth from oil.

122

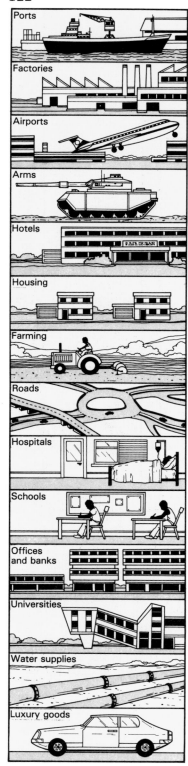

Ports

Factories

Airports

Arms

Hotels

Housing

Farming

Roads

Hospitals

Schools

Offices and banks

Universities

Water supplies

Luxury goods

Fig. 10.12
Using the wealth from oil

Exercise 10.6

Study the drawings in Figure 10.12 and the photographs in Figure 10.13.

(a) Which of the uses of oil money shown are likely to benefit the ordinary people of the Persian Gulf?

(b) Which of the uses might be described as 'prestige projects' designed to impress other countries?

(c) Which of the developments will require much money to spend on manufactured goods made in developed countries?

(d) Do you consider the money from oil to have been spent wisely? Give reasons for your answer.

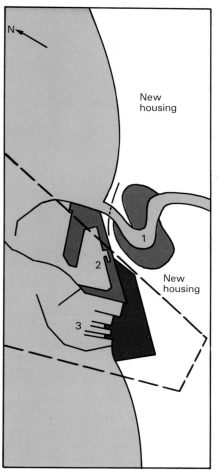

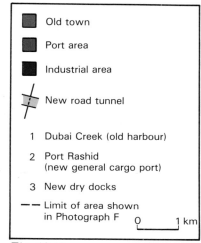

Old town

Port area

Industrial area

New road tunnel

1 Dubai Creek (old harbour)

2 Port Rashid (new general cargo port)

3 New dry docks

– – Limit of area shown in Photograph F

0   1 km

Fig. 10.13
Changing Dubai
(a) Dubai Fort, now a museum
(b) Dubai Creek and town. Notice the new road which tunnels under the creek.
(c) Old harbour, Dubai Creek, with new office blocks in the background
(d) Dubai International Airport
(e) New dry docks and ship repair yard. The central dry dock can take oil tankers of one million tonnes.
(f) Dry docks, Port Rashid and new housing and industrial areas

Exercise 10.7

(a) Place a piece of tracing paper over Photograph (f) in Figure 10.13. Trace the coastline and breakwaters in blue and the major roads in red. Lightly pencil in the horizon.

(b) Refer to Figure 10.13 and then shade the port area, the industrial area and the new housing area in different colours. Label Port Rashid and the dry docks.

(c) Add a key to your trace and give it the heading 'New Developments in Dubai'.

(b)

(f)

The need for labour and technical help

The rapid development of the Persian Gulf countries cannot be achieved with money alone. A large labour supply is needed to build the new roads, ports, buildings, oil installations and industrial plants. Several of the countries have very small populations and so labour from other countries has been brought in to work on construction sites (Figure 10.14) and in the oilfields. The oil producers have been especially short of highly trained, skilled people for work both in the oil industry and in the other new developments. They have therefore had to turn to the developed countries. For example, the large harbour and dry-docks project at Dubai, shown in Figure 10.13 was built jointly by two British engineering companies, Costain International and Taylor Woodrow International. Seven hundred and thirty engineers and other skilled staff from Britain and other countries were employed, together with 5950 construction workers from India and Pakistan.

Fig. 10.14
Work in progress on the construction of Dubai dry docks

Exercise 10.8
(a) Suggest why the oil producers are short of highly trained, skilled people.
(b) Which jobs needing a high level of skill or education do Figures 10.12 and 10.13 suggest may be required?
(c) How will people from the developed countries be attracted to work in the Middle East?
(d) Suggest why the construction companies have found India and Pakistan good areas to recruit labour.
(e) The oil producers hope that in the future they will be able to provide skilled and well-educated people themselves. What evidence is there is Figure 10.12 to suggest this?

Problems of water supply

The increasing proportion of the population of oil-producing countries in towns, the movement to the area of foreign workers, the rising living standards and the growth of industry have given rise to another problem—providing water.

Desalination plants which produce fresh water from sea water have been built. Such plants are a very expensive way of producing fresh water, as fuel must be burnt to heat the sea water. It is necessary to use this method because supplies of natural fresh water are very limited indeed. For the future, it has even been suggested that fresh water may be obtained from icebergs towed from the Antarctic.

Exercise 10.9

(a) Why is the natural fresh water supply so limited?
(b) Suggest why a desalination plant may be operated at a lower cost by the Persian Gulf than in many other parts of the world.
(c) What problems can you see in the proposed use of icebergs from the Antarctic for fresh water?

When the oil runs out

The oil producers rely almost completely on oil for their prosperity. However, the oil reserves will not last for ever and there are very few areas left in these countries where prospecting for oil has not taken place. Some people have criticised the oil producers for building prestige projects such as international airports and luxury hotels, saying there will be little use for them when the oil has gone. In order to lessen the heavy reliance on oil, the oil producers have attempted to develop manufacturing industry. As most of the oil producers have small populations, export industries must be developed.

Figure 10.15 lists the things that Bahrain, one of the Persian Gulf states with a relatively small population, has been able to do by way of industrial development. Bahrain has been the main centre of trade in the region for many years and so started its industrialisation with an important advantage over some of its neighbours. It also has the most important international airport in the Persian Gulf area.

Oil refining
Chemicals
Aluminium smelting
Building materials
Soft drinks
Clothing
Plastics
Ship repairing

Fig. 10.15 Bahrain's industries

Exercise 10.10

(a) Look back at the map of the Middle East (Figure 10.2). What advantage has the position of Bahrain as the centre of trade within the region?
(b) Make a list of Bahrain's industries from Figure 10.15 under the following headings:
(i) industries connected with oil;
(ii) industries not connected with oil.
Would you consider Bahrain to have a good selection of industries for the future when oil begins to run out?
(c) In Exercise 10.5, Bahrain appeared as a residual on the graph showing oil production per person plotted against average income per person. It showed that average income was higher than one might expect from the figure of oil production per person. Considering what you have learnt about Bahrain, attempt to explain this.

Growing wealth outside the Middle East

The growth of wealth is not restricted to the oil producers of the Middle East. We have already mentioned another example— Singapore. However, in most other cases, the new-found wealth is limited to a small section of the population or rapid industrial development is limited to only certain regions of a country.

126

In Asia, several countries are following Singapore in the development of export industries, making electrical goods and precision instruments, or have developed the manufacture of textiles and clothing for export. Hong Kong, South Korea and Taiwan are examples. Many of the factories belong to Japanese and American companies. Despite these developments, problems of housing, unemployment and poverty remain.

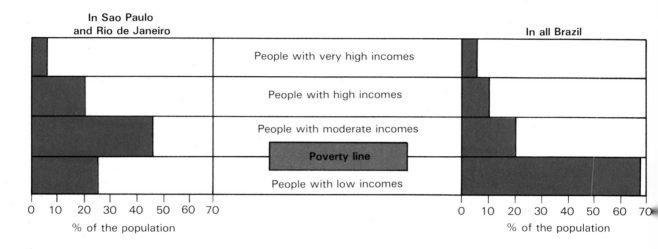

In Sao Paulo and Rio de Janeiro

In all Brazil

- People with very high incomes
- People with high incomes
- People with moderate incomes
- **Poverty line**
- People with low incomes

% of the population

% of the population

Fig. 10.16
The distribution of wealth in Brazil

Brazil is the largest and most industrialised of the South American countries, but wealth is concentrated among certain sections of the population and in certain regions. The south-east is relatively rich and wealth from coffee and resources such as iron ore has been invested in industry. On the other hand, the north-east of Brazil is very poor. Figure 10.16 shows how wealth is distributed among different sections of the population in Sao Paulo and Rio de Janeiro, the largest cities and industrial centres, and among the population of Brazil generally. The distribution of wealth in these cities is similar to that of many developed countries. The city has many industries which are typical of developed countries: textiles, engineering, electrical goods and the manufacture of motor vehicles.

Fig. 10.17
South America

1. The wealth produced by Mexico's farming, mineral development and industry increases by 6 to 7% every year.

2. Between 1960 and 1970 the income of factory workers increased by 70%.

3. Between 1960 and 1970 the income of landless farm labourers fell by 15%.

4. Mexico's population has doubled over the last 25 years.

5. Unemployment is increasing rapidly.

Fig. 10.18
Changes in Mexico

Yet Sao Paulo and Rio de Janeiro have many problems typical of cities in the Third World; very rapid growth, shanty towns and lack of planning. The distribution of wealth in all Brazil is typical of the Third World with many people existing at a low standard of living.

Fig. 10.19
Rio de Janeiro.

Exercise 10.11
Mexico is another example of a country where growing wealth is affecting only part of the population. Figure 10.18 shows some of the changes which have taken place in Mexico in recent years.
(a)   From the information in Figure 10.18 explain why it is said that the gap between rich and poor is widening.
(b)   What changes for the better are taking place in Mexico? What changes for the worse are taking place?
(c)   What would you consider is the main obstacle to the solving of Mexico's problems in the future?

Summary

Oil has been the main cause of growing wealth in a few developing countries. The population of the rich oil producers is, however, only a very small proportion of the total population of the Third World, and so this growing wealth has affected only a relatively small number of people. The wealth has been invested in new services such as schools and hospitals, and in farming and industry.

Increasing wealth has also been a feature of some developing countries which are not oil producers. Some Asian countries are developing export industries and hope to follow the example of Japan. However, increasing wealth is often concentrated into a limited area of a country or affects only a small section of the population. In many parts of the Third World, the gap between the rich and poor is increasing and 'development' does not keep pace with the rapid growth of population.

INDEX OF KEY IDEAS

Key idea	Chapter 1	Chapter 2	Chapter 3	Chapter 4	Chapter 5	Chapter 6	Chapter 7	Chapter 8	Chapter 9	Chapter 10
Accessibility			Land use patterns		Location of export crop production	Accessibility of mineral deposits	Location of ports, Hinterlands			Oil field development
Classification		Types of farm		Types of farm	Types of farm	Different minerals, Types of mine	Different ports	Different ways of developing the land	Types of industry	
Change	Overcoming the environment	Man changing the environment	Changes in farming	Changes in farming	Changes in farming	New source of minerals	Port development	Improving farming, 'Green Revolution'	Housing problems, Redevelopment	Growing wealth, Changes in the Middle East
Distribution	Distribution of crops		Land use patterns	Population, land use patterns		Distribution of mining	Hinterlands		Distribution of cities, land use in cities	Distribution of oil production
Environment	Environmental relationships, climatic patterns	Rain forests, changes by man	Areas affected by drought	Tropical highlands, Vegetation zones		Impact of mining	Location of ports	Overcoming problems of environment		Problems of water supply
Growth		Effects of population growth		Tourism	Expansion of crop production	Expansion of mineral production	Growth of ports, Industrial growth	Population growth, Expansion of farming	Growth of cities, Industrial growth	Growing wealth, growth of ports and cities
Location	Locations of villages	Locations of farms	Planning land use on a farm	Locations of farms	Locations of plantations	Location of mineral production	Location of ports	Location of irrigation schemes	Patterns in cities	Location of oil terminals
Movement		Shifting agriculture	Wildlife migration, Nomads		Trade in export crops	Trade in minerals	Movement to and from ports		Movement to cities	
Networks	Transport networks	Transport networks			Transport networks	Transport networks	Transport networks	Improving transport links		Oil pipeline networks
Systems	The Ecosystem, Hydrological cycle	Farming systems		Farming systems	Patterns of trade			Vicious circles of poverty and ill-health		